CHOICES:

Exercises in Critical Thinking

C. Michael Botterweck & B. Rimmel-Kwidd

StarPoint Press
Elmhurst, Illinois 60126

CHOICES:
Exercises in Critical Thinking

Design, Production and Typesetting by StarPoint Press

Typeface: New Century Schoolbook

Executive Editor: B. Rimmel-Kwidd

Cover Art: Robert V. Rimmel

Graphic Design: Suzanne Jacobs-Fabian

ISBN # 1-886202-08-7

Copyright © 2000 by StarPoint Press
297 May Street
Elmhurst, Il   60126

Acknowledgements

Neither of us would be the people that we are if it were not for each other and for the people in our families who helped to shape us. So, first we must thank all of them: our mothers and our fathers, our brothers and their wives and children, and perhaps most of all, our sons—Josh (and Debbie) and Jesse Kwidd and Bruce and Brian Botterweck.

And then there are the students, hundreds of them, who each have a story, a case that they live, day by day. They are the ones that inspire us, motivate our work. It is for them that we stay up late and get up early and keep notepads by our bedsides to jot down another good idea or point to bring to class.

Finally, a special thanks to Robert V. Rimmel (1922-1998), the father of one of your authors and the artist who created the cover art for this text and several of our other works. We all miss you. *Heb di sorg, Babe.*

TABLE OF CONTENTS

Preface

Before you begin turning the pages of *Choices* we thought a few introductory comments might be in order. First, of all of our writing, this textbook is very special to us. It is not a textbook in the traditional sense of providing information and theoretical frameworks. It is much more. It is a book about people, everyday people such as yourself. Within the pages and stories are people who face the everyday challenges life presents. These are not perfect people, they are real people with all the flaws and frailties that come with being human. Within these stories you will see yourself or others close to you. In each story, the main character is presented with a life challenge and must make a difficult and agonizing decision. In *Choices* there are no endings. It will be your task to place yourself into the position of this person and resolve the dilemma. Be forewarned, the decisions will be difficult and in many cases you will not be happy with your choices. Nevertheless, a decision will be required.

Our second comment addresses the issue of why we chose to write *Choices* and why we believe it is worth your time and energy to read and agonize over the stories in this book. As educators we are concerned with what we believe to be an undue emphasis reading and memorizing information without any ability to use it. Certainly, information is important. However, even more important is the ability to use information. What we refer to here is the ability to think critically and solve problems. This is exactly the point of *Choices*, to provide a framework in which students can learn to think critically and use information constructively. This is what we believe to be the true goal of education.

Third, in attempting to resolve the dilemmas you'll face in *Choices*, try to avoid the quick and simple solution. Human beings are complicated creatures and so are the solutions to the stories in *Choices*. Each problem you will encounter will be multifaceted. What this means is that to truly resolve the problem you must understand its moral, political, economical, psychological and social dimensions. This is no easy task, but not to do so will leave you with an incomplete solution.

And fourth, in discussing the stories in *Choices* with your classmates or friends, keep in mind that everyone sees life a bit differently. While you may come to a decision that you feel comfortable with, others will not. In other words, expect disagreement. This is the nature of the social sciences. We could bring twenty renowned social scientists to your classroom, give them one of the case stories to resolve, and find tremendous disagreement among them as to what the right solution is.

With these points in mind, it's now time for you to embark upon your journey. Along the way you will undoubtedly become frustrated. Don't despair, in the context of learning, frustration is the first step in the problem solving process. Try to keep in mind the prophetic words of Muhammad Ali, "The man who views the world at 50 the same as he did at 20 has wasted 30 years of his life." Our hope is that in some small way *Choices* will contribute to a more fulfilling and enlightened life for you. Have fun.

American Made

Ellen peered into the brightly-lit hallway from the sanctuary of the darkened hospital room where her daughter, Emily, slept. Her body shielded by the heavy door, only her face was visible. She calculated her chances for success to be slim. Not that it mattered. Even with the odds against her she knew she had to at least try; had to do something to give Emily some kind of a chance. Emily was recovered and ready to go home tomorrow, but she might not be so lucky the next time. The simple tonsillectomy was one of the few medical procedures she was entitled to. Next time, some more urgent procedure might be denied and her child would be allowed to die. Taking a deep breath she stepped momentarily out into the light, and just as quickly disappeared again into the room two doors down.

Eighteen month-old Mae Koslick was at Elmhurst Memorial because of the drunk driver who had hit her Auntie Anne's car. Her mom and dad were recovering from their injuries on another floor of the hospital and she had been strapped to her life-support system and traction bars for the past three days. Earlier this morning, the machine that did her breathing for her since the accident had been removed and her legs were freed from their metal prison. Although Mae was breathing on her own now. Still, she had not awakened from the coma induced by the trauma to her head. But, everyone hoped that she would do so sometime tomorrow or the next day. Although no one was making any real comments to the family, Ellen had overheard the doctors doing their morning rounds. And she'd gotten the little red headed nurse to tell her what she knew. The conclusion was that Mae would live, but she'd never walk again and they suspected that she'd be, at minimum, brain damaged at a level that would never allow her to function beyond what was normal for a ten year-old.

"What an absolute tragedy for a perfectly healthy little girl," the nurse, shaking her head slowly, had said. Ellen interpreted it to mean, "too bad it wasn't your damaged baby in the car wreck instead."

Ellen stood, dead still, just inside the tightly closed door breathing short, shallow breaths. Her tenure at the hospital made her well aware of the routine. No one would be here to check on Mae. The limited night staff was on their lunch hour in the break room. At three in the morning only emergencies set off by screaming machines, or hysterical patients or their parents, were answered. Mae, with no one to watch over her, disconnected from her apparatus earlier today and in a solid coma, presented no danger of either happening. Yet, although time was on her side, Ellen didn't want to be here long. She wanted to get it over with. She knew what she had to do and she was about to do it. It was her daughter's only chance. Panic and terror settled into a place removed from her own being. In their stead, solid and unmoving, had settled a steely resolve to do the unthinkable. After a minute her vision adjusted perfectly to the darkness. She moved quietly across the shiny floor and stood looking down on the tiny, perfectly still Mae. As she watched the little girl breathe, she tried not to be moved by the wispy hair and the translucent skin. She tried not to notice the pulse of type 0 positive blood, a perfect match to her own daughter's, beating a fast tattoo in the little girl's turned up wrist. Tried not to see the little fist that curled tightly, hanging-on to whatever bits of life were left to her. Instead, Ellen's eyes shifted to the wall above the little girl's head and settled on the clip-on that held the card.

The card. The card that would give Emily a chance. The card Ellen would do anything to get. The card. The only thing that mattered. Too bad she couldn't just steal it and walk away.

But that would never work. A missing card was a crisis that would call for investigations and a sequence of events that would make the card invalid and, as a result, impossible to use. An invalid card was of no use to her. What she needed was a card that she could pass off as her daughter's. Emily was older than Mae by almost four months, but that didn't matter. Neither child had hit the crucial 24-month age where fingerprints were required and placed onto one of the many chips inside the card that contained information used to identify citizens of the United States of America.

The card, issued at birth, was given to the parents of the newborn child as they left the birthing center. It contained information that was once listed on that old, thing of the past, birth certificate. Also noted was any pertinent medical information. Medical details were added and updated each time the child was checked-up, immunized, or treated. At two years of age, fingerprints solidified identity. The information on the card would eventually be used to identify a citizen as an employable person, a convicted felon, an insurable driver, and much more. It would allow or disallow access to higher education predicated on school testing and success. It would hold dozens of bits of personal information that enable access to services, programs, goods, travel, and a host of other critical advantages or disadvantages.

Later on, the card would be used by employers to deposit paychecks and as a way to pay for anything from groceries to tolls. Income tax information, passport identification, marital status, and much more was added to the card as time went on. The chips sandwiched between the layers of plastic determined everything from who you were to what you would be allowed to become. The card was everything that you needed.

Initiated as a means of ensuring that American jobs went to Americans and American tax dollars, collected to guarantee medical insurance for Americans, went only to Americans, it had become so much more than that. It had become everything anyone was about. It only stopped meaning anything when you died, at which time it was erased; became inactive, null, and void.

The limited information contained on the card of the little girl that lay in the bed an arm's length away said that she was in perfect health. Soon, once her new condition was determined and verified, new limiting information would be added. But not yet. As of now, there were no restrictions as to what treatment she might or might not receive. She was in perfect health. Something her own Emily had never been. After the car crash that killed her aunt and injured her parents, Mae was given full access to medical services because she had been lucky enough to have been born perfect.

In her daughter Emily's case, although she was healthy at present, her genetic history made her ineligible for many medical procedures. Hard won medical dollars would only be expended on those who would most likely benefit. Emily's case had been deemed too risky. No reason to spend limited funds on one who was genetically inferior and likely to die. The fact that she would in all probability—bean counters had estimated that chance at 80 percent—develop a cancer before her 20th birthday, automatically denied her medical attention of all but the most basic kind. Beyond that, only intervention designed to alleviate pain was allowed.

The bottom line was that if anything ever happened to Emily, she'd be out of luck. If she had been the one in the car wreck, they would have only given her limited care. Emily would have died.

Mae, however, had lived. Now she was going to have to die so that Emily would have a chance to live in the future. Even when she developed the deadly cancer that they expected, it would be viewed as an unexplained, unexpected turn of events. Not something for which treatment would be denied. Mae's card would give Emily the chance at medical care. And that, in turn, would give her a very good chance to survive.

Ellen grabbed Mae's card and replaced it with her daughter's knowing full well that when they discovered that Mae had died in the night, the doctor who declared her dead was mandated to immediately run the card over the sensor gun he carried in his pocket. This would, without ceremony, activate the chip that invalidated the card, her daughter's card, by erasing all the information on it. No one would check the card before deactivating it. That wasn't part of the procedure. Once it was erased, it was all over. Mae's life was over, but Emily's card would be the one erased. And because of it, Emily would become Mae and have her chance to live. A minor move and new friends and neighbors would welcome Ellen and the newly renamed Mae as part of the neighborhood, the community. It would be easy to explain the differences in last names should she ever be called upon to do so. Divorce, remarriage, even adoption, any number of things would explain the difference in their last names.

Ellen looked down at the little girl who, if she lived, would be brain damaged and paraplegic and thought of her own Emily. Tears were flowing from her eyes as she reached out and touched the little girl. Her decision was made.

American Made   Name_____

Instructions: read each statement before coming to class. Indicate your response by circling "agree" or "disagree" at the end of the statement. In class, discuss the statement with your group and attempt to reach consensus. If consensus is impossible record your vote and write *your* individual response to the statement in three or more complete sentences.

1. Emily has a better chance to live a quality life. Therefore, it is morally right for Ellen to do whatever is necessary to see that her daughter gets the card. Agree or Disagree. **Group Vote: Agree_____ Disagree _____**

2. Immigrants can't expect to receive the same rights and privileges as those who are citizens of this nation. Agree or Disagree. **Group Vote: Agree_____ Disagree _____**

3. The trouble with America is that it allows too many people to immigrate to this country without the means to care for themselves. Agree or Disagree. **Group Vote: Agree_____ Disagree _____**

4. People who choose to give birth to defective children should not expect the taxpayers to support their medical needs, e.g., preemies, drug-addicted, mentally or physically disabled babies, etc. Agree or Disagree. **Group Vote: Agree_____ Disagree _____**

5. The ID card is a good idea! It will keep people who take American jobs and medical dollars out of the US. Agree or Disagree. **Group Vote: Agree_____ Disagree _____**

6. The impact of this kind of technological "know-how" advances society. It may not be perfect or kind to some individuals, but the good of the whole society is more important than the lives of the few. Agree or Disagree. **Group Vote: Agree_____ Disagree_____**

7. Once the technology is available, parents should be forced to genetically alter or abort their defective unborn children so as to ensure that they do not become a burden to society. Agree or Disagree. **Group Vote: Agree_____ Disagree_____**

8. It is stupid to waste hundreds of thousands of dollars on sustaining Mae's life when the money could be better spent helping other needy children capable of living normal lives. Agree or disagree. **Group Vote: Agree_____ Disagree_____**

9. The real problem is that medical advances are bound to spill over into all aspects of our lives—what jobs you can obtain, who you can marry, where you can live, the right to give birth, etc. Agree or Disagree. **Group Vote: Agree_____ Disagree _____**

10. Despite all the potential problems we are helpless to stop the advance and use of science. Agree or Disagree. **Group Vote: Agree_____ Disagree_____**

Question #1: If you were Ellen, would take the life of Mae to ensure that your child could receive the medical help she will need in the future?

Question # 2: Do you believe that innovations in genetic therapy will help or harm the human race? List some potential advantages and disadvantages of gene therapy.

_____
_____
_____
_____
_____
_____
_____
_____
_____
_____
_____
_____
_____
_____
_____
_____
_____
_____
_____
_____
_____
_____
_____
_____
_____
_____
_____
_____
_____
_____

Angie's Day

Angie Robbins pinched a lock of hair over her forehead and twisted it into a tight curl. Misting it lightly, she held it in place for a moment until she was confident that it would hold the set. She stood in front of the mirror admiring the cut. For fifteen years she had worn her hair in what she laughingly referred to as the housewife special. It was easy to manage, didn't need expensive gels to maintain, and required only an occasional cut. This cut, although shorter, would require more attention and cash. Fortunately, her friend Linda, the much-in-demand hair stylist, did free cuts in her off-hours for family and close friends. Never could she have afforded what they extorted at the glitzy salon on Michigan Avenue where Linda worked. Moving to her closet she withdrew the dark blue jacket and skirt suit she had purchased a month ago. It was perfectly cut to exude an aura of feminine beauty and maturity. It was just the image she wanted to project for this important interview that would launch her new life. She had purchased it at Nordstrom where it had been, thankfully, on sale. She laughed silently remembering the day she had discovered it on the closeout rack. Immediately after laying eyes on it she held it tightly to her breast as she scurried to the checkout counter where she stood in absolute terror that the clerk would somehow discover that a mistake had been made and that the suit was not discounted. If so, she could never have afforded the ungodly sum demanded on the original price tag.

Yes, she thought, things were finally going her way. Having dropped out of college to support her husband's education and then the years of raising the kids, it was finally coming around to her time. Not that she minded the years. They were good years. Paul was a wonderful husband, a giving man. Had there been money they would have both finished their education. But money was short and they had already decided to have children so it was important for Paul to finish so that he could support the family. And Jim and Cheryl were good kids. She had derived great satisfaction from raising her children. Both she and Paul had felt it was important to have a full-time parent in the house. The world presented so many potential pitfalls for children. Parents needed to be vigilant and present in their children's lives to provide the guidance necessary to steer them to the right path. And she had done exactly that for nearly eighteen years. Then, two years ago, when her son turned sixteen and her daughter fourteen, she returned to college to complete an Associates degree in capital investment at the local community college. In the spring, Jim would graduate from high school and Cheryl would enter her junior year. Yes, she thought again, things were moving along. Paul was in line for a well-deserved promotion at work, Jim had been accepted at Northwestern, and she had an interview with a respected real-estate investment firm. Her mentor at the college, Professor Herring, had advanced her name to a close friend who was president of the firm. It was a chance of a lifetime for someone in her position. She was hungry for a change, a chance to prove herself. Also, the money was desperately needed for Jim's tuition at Northwestern. Most of her salary would go for that. But it wasn't the money that she craved, it was the excitement of a new life.

As she was about to collect her purse and leave for her interview the phone rang.

"Is this Mrs. Robbins?" inquired the voice on the phone.

"Yes."

"This is Martha Wright at the community senior care center."

Angie's chest tightened. Paul's mother, Gertie, spent the day at the center and nights at their place since her husband's death six months ago. She suffered from dementia and was unable to care for herself without supervision. They had moved her into the their house temporarily until they could evaluate the care and facilities she would need. The senior care center seemed to be a perfect solution. It was inexpensive, clean, and staffed with caring people. It also allowed Angie the time she needed to finish her education.

"Is something wrong? Is Gertie okay?" asked Angie quickly.

"She's missing again. It appears that she walked out with some guest when we weren't looking. Has she been taking her medications?"

"I think so, but one time I did catch her trying to sneak them out of her mouth when I wasn't looking. We had a talk and she agreed not to do it again."

"We notified the police." The woman paused. "I think you need to come down here. When we do find her she's going to be confused."

"I have an interview, but let me get in touch with my husband. He's closer to the center."

Agnie quickly dialed Paul's office. No, he was not in the office the secretary informed her. He and several others had left the firm to attend an important meeting with a potential customer across town. He wasn't due back until late in the afternoon. Paul's supervisor, Jerry Griggs, had left strict orders not to interrupt them. However, offered the secretary, if it was an emergency she was sure Mr. Griggs would understand. Angie's mind raced frantically. No, she replied, it wasn't an emergency. Hanging up, she dialed the number of the real estate investment firm where she was to interview. Apologizing, she explained the situation to personal director, Naomi Smith, and asked for a time later in the day. Much to her relief, the woman was sympathetic and changed the time to mid-afternoon. Angie sat back in her chair and tried to calm her racing heart. Ten minutes later she had changed to jeans and a sweatshirt and was racing out the door to the senior care center.

Pulling into the parking lot, Angie noticed a police car parked at the entrance. She parked and rushed up the steps. Entering, she rounded the corner and headed down the corridor to the supervisor's office. Martha Wright was engaged in a conversation with a young policewoman. Looking up, the woman caught sight of Angie and quickly rose. Taking Angie's arm she ushered her over to the police officer and introduced the two. Officer Sutton, she explained, had found Gertie wandering through one of the city parks about six blocks from the center. The officer explained that while Gertie appeared disoriented, she was calm and in a pleasant mood and looking for her husband, Bill. Angie explained to the officer that Bill had died six months ago and that Gertie suffered symptoms of early dementia. As long as Gertie took her medicine she was fine, but apparently she had not taken the medication or had not received the proper dose. Angie apologized for the inconvenience and pledged that they would call Gertie's doctor to re-evaluate the situation. The officer was gracious, explaining that her own mother had experienced a similar situation with her grandmother. The officer offered her support and then left the two women alone.

"I want to thank you for your understanding, Martha," offered Angie. "I'd better go now and check on Gertie. Paul will pick her up at the usual time."

"Angie," called the woman before she reached the door. "Perhaps you and I should have a talk about Gertie."

"Is there something else?" asked Angie as she turned back to the woman. "I thought the officer said she's fine now."

"It's not that simple," she said gesturing Angie to one of the battered leather chairs. "I think we need to talk about Gertie's future."

"Future," gasped Angie struggling for breath, fearful at what was to follow.

"You know Dr. Simmons, don't you?"

Angie nodded. One of the nurses had pointed him out to her once, explaining that while he was not on staff he was called in to evaluate critical cases. A visit by Dr. Simmons was not a good sign.

"His specialty is geriatrics and he's an expert on dementia. As you recall, the center has the right to independently evaluate those under our care. It's for everyone's protection. I'm sure you understand."

Angie nodded.

"We had Dr. Simmons evaluate Gertie the other day."

"Have there been problems?"

"I'm afraid so," stated Martha. "We've had several incidents with Gertie besides the one today. It seems that she has been clogging the toilets with paper. Mind you, it's not a malicious act. She just doesn't seem to be able to judge her use of paper when she relieves herself. In fact, the last time we had to resort to calling out a plumber, a cost we can ill-afford. Then, last week she closed the stopper in the bathroom sink and left the water running causing a minor flood. Two days ago, she wandered into the kitchen area and lit a burner on the stove. Fortunately, one of the staff found it before a fire started or anyone was accidentally burned. That's when I asked Dr. Simmons to evaluate her."

"And?" asked Angie nervously.

"Simply put, she needs more care than we can provide," answered the woman. "By no means are we saying that Gertie is lost. It's just that she needs constant supervision. She has good days, and she has not-so-good days. That's going to be true even if she does take her medication."

"What's the long term prognosis?"

"I asked Dr. Simmons about that and he says there is no way to tell. She could go on this way for years." Martha Wright flipped through the pages of Gertie's folder. "How old is Gertie? I don't think I have it in the file."

"Honestly, we're not sure," answered Angie. "She is a holocaust survivor. As I'm sure you're aware, the Nazis destroyed all records. Gertie will tell you that she's seventy-five, but we suspect she's subtracted a few birthdays. Vanity, you know."

Martha Wright smiled. "Wish I could do the same. Anyway, let's assume she is in her late seventies, she could easily live in this state for another decade, possibly two. Other than the dementia, she's in great health."

Angie sat quietly.

Martha leaned forward in her chair. "These are not easy decisions. As I see it, you have only a couple of choices. You can send her to a nursing home or you can care for her in your own home. If you decide to take care of her in your home, you can hire a private nurse during the day."

"But the expense," protested Angie.

"I won't mislead you, private nursing care is very costly. Few people can afford it." Martha Wright walked over and put a hand on Angie's shoulder. "I feel bad about this, but the rules require me to ask you to take Gertie home now."

On the way home Angie's mind was again racing. Her interview was scheduled for three that afternoon. Paul was unreachable. There was only one choice. At two-thirty she sped up to the school with Gertie in the backseat. Making sure the doors of the car were locked and explaining to Gertie that she'd be just a minute, she raced inside to the office and asked the secretary to call her daughter, Cheryl. A minute later, the two were arguing in the hallway outside the office.

"Mom," protested the girl. "I have band practice and then afterwards we were all going over to Kathy's house to rehearse for play tryouts tomorrow. This isn't fair. Why don't you ask Jim?"

"Jim has baseball practice," answer the woman. "He has a chance for a scholarship. We need that scholarship to help pay his tuition."

"So, I get dumped on," argued the girl.

"No you don't get dumped on," answered Angie. "You get the chance to help out. Now, don't argue with me anymore. The decision is made. Let's go!"

"I hope you're not planning on sticking me with a full-time babysitting job," complained the girl. "I have a life, just like Jim does."

At ten to three Angie pulled into the parking lot of Land Investments Unlimited. The architectural structure gleamed with vision and success. Seeing the building and thinking of the possibilities made her heart ache with desire. A new start, a new life, thought Angie. If only she could impress Naomi Smith as much as she had her professors at the college. She closed her eyes and commanded her body and mind to calm and focus on the task ahead. Five minutes later she stood at the receptionist's desk. The young man logged her arrival and then asked her to take a seat. A moment later a slender, attractive woman with short silver hair appeared. "Hi," she said extending her hand, "I'm Naomi Smith."

Angie rose and shook her hand. "Hello, I'm Angie Robbins."

"Of course," she replied, smiling warmly. "Why don't we go back to my office."

The woman's office was not auspiciously large. This was of no surprise to Angie since Professor Herring had warned her that Land Investments Unlimited valued substance and achievement over flash and fluff. Nevertheless, though somewhat on the small side, the office was warmly decorated with attention to detail. It was the type of office that welcomed rather than intimidated its visitors. Looking about, Angie decided that it was just the kind of look she would choose for her own office if she were lucky enough to land the position. Of course, she reminded herself, she would not get an office immediately. More than likely she would be placed at a desk in an open area with others. But, in time, with hard work and a determined spirit she could move up and then, one day, she would have her own office. Yes, she could wait. After all, she had waited most of her life.

"Would you like some coffee, Mrs. Robbins," asked Naomi Smith.

"Please, call me Angie," she requested. "And as for coffee, I'd love some, but I think I'm too nervous to hold the cup without spilling it."

The older woman laughed. "I remember my first interview, even though it was decades ago. God, I was so scared I could hardly talk. I even stumbled on the rug on the way to the personnel director's office and sprained my ankle. He had to help me into the office and into a chair. So you couldn't do any worse than that."

"Did you get the job?"

"I did," she replied smiling. "Once he got me settled, we both started laughing until we cried. It helps to be a bit on the human side." The woman pushed a button on the intercom. "Tom," she instructed, "could you please bring in a couple cups of coffee and make sure they're only half full."

"Cream and sugar?"

Naomi looked at Angie who shook her head.

"Not necessary, Tom. Thanks."

Almost instantly the man appeared with two steaming cups on a tray. The coffee smelled good and had a soothing effect.

"Speaking of being human," began the woman looking over Angie's file, "that's exactly how Professor Herring describes you. In addition, he states that you are a quick learner, hard working, and very organized." The woman paused to read. "Hmmm," she murmured, tapping the file with a pencil.

"Is something wrong?" asked Angie anxiously.

"Oh, no," the older woman replied. "On the contrary, this is the best recommendation the Professor has ever written. Usually he's not so charitable. You must have really impressed the old bird."

Seeing the startled expression on Angie's face, the older woman laughed. "Oh, I thought you knew that the Professor and I are old friends. We've spent a lifetime goading each other."

Angie relaxed again.

"Let's talk about you, Angie. Tell me about your life. What's going on now. What do you really want? Where do you want to be in five years, in ten years?" For over an hour Angie recounted her life, interest, dreams, and future goals. It was nearly five when Naomi Smith closed Angie's folder.

"Interesting," she mused softly. "I usually don't do this but in your case an exception is in order. I'm going to recommend your addition to the firm. However, I want you to be aware that your life is going to change dramatically. You'll have to prove yourself. That means some long hours. And you do realize that we have investments out of state, don't you? You'll need to travel and it may be unpredictable, not something you can plan for. When you get the call, you'll have to be ready to go just like anyone else who works for this firm. As far as salary, with no work experience I'm forced to start you at the bottom. Of course, over time your salary will increase commensurate with your experience and financial worth to the company. That's the way it works. If you can handle all that, welcome aboard."

Angie thanked her and was about to leave when the older woman stopped her. "May I ask a personal question?"

Angie sat back down.

"When you called earlier in the day you mentioned your mother-in-law has dementia. I was unclear as to whether she lived with you or in a home?"

"She lives with us for now," replied Angie. "Her husband passed away six months ago."

"What are your plans for her?"

"We haven't really decided," answered Angie.

The older woman nodded before responding. "This may not be any of my business, but I would be remiss not to say something."

"About my mother-in-law?" questioned Angie, confused.

"About you, Angie," she replied. "In my years of experience, I've seen many women's careers ruined by situations exactly like yours. For whatever reason, right or wrong, women usually get stuck with caring for elderly relatives. I suspect it's just because we're born nurturers. There's nothing inherently bad about it, but it does limit our career options. This is a high stakes business. Lots of money is on the line. When you're needed, you have to be there for us. Otherwise, we lose and the people we're responsible to lose—big time. I've seen women try to balance work and care responsibilities. They try to patch together a system of part-time care providers, senior centers, friends, and all sorts of fall-back provisions. But invariably situations arise and work suffers."

"Are you saying I should put my mother-in-law in a nursing home?" asked Angie.

"I'm not telling you what to do," responded the woman. "That's a decision you and your husband must make. But it's something I would give serious thought. Nursing homes, many of them, are not all that bad. And from what you tell me, your mother-in-law needs extensive help."

"I'll talk with Paul tonight," promised Angie. "In reality, it was something I knew we'd have to face anyway."

"Good," replied the woman.

Angie stood and walked to the door. Before opening the door she turned to the older woman. "May I ask something?"

"Certainly."

"What happens if we decide to keep my mother-in-law in our home?"

"I'll be honest with you Angie," responded the woman, "Mr. Hutton, our president, has had a couple of bad experiences with women trying to balance work, kids, and parents. We've lost a couple of big deals. He's going to ask me about your situation. I can't lie. Maybe it's best if I give you a couple of days before I put your name forward."

"Is there someone else you have in mind for this job?"

"There's a young man right out of college. He interviews very well."

"Is he married?"

"Yes," she answered and then added, "he has two children and a wife who is a full-time homemaker."

"That was me twenty years ago."

"I know," replied the woman.

Angie arrived home to find her daughter in tears. "Where's your grandmother?" she asked.

"Upstairs in her room and I don't care if she ever comes out," she cried. "I hope she stays up there forever, the old bitch."

"Don't swear and don't call your grandmother that," reprimanded Angie.

"Well, she is!"

"Okay," asked Angie, "what's the problem?"

"The problem," coughed the girl through tears, "is that she destroyed my relationship with Barry and embarrassed me to death. I'm never going to be able to go to school again."

"What happened?"

"I was talking to Barry on the telephone when suddenly she cuts in on the conversation. She had been listening all along to every word we said. Then she begins to call him names and tells him she knows what he really wants and that I'm a good Christian girl. She tells him never to call or come over again." Throwing herself onto the sofa the girl began to sob. "This is going to get all over school. Everyone will be laughing at me. I'm ruined!"

Angie rubbed her daughter's back. "Listen, your grandmother is having a bad day. I'll talk to her. It won't happen again."

Paul arrived home early, around five-thirty. His mood was buoyant. He kissed Angie and then danced her around the kitchen to announce, "We got the contract! The largest contract in the history of the company! Old man Griggs was so pleased he announced my promotion on the spot. As of next week I'll be the new Sales Director for the entire Midwest Region. Finally, after all these years, the big break." Wrapping his arms around his wife's waist he said, "Okay, let's hear about your interview. I bet you knocked them dead, right?"

Angie smiled.

"I knew it! I just knew it!" he exclaimed, dancing her around again. "You got the job! When do you start?"

Angie took a deep breath. She had planned to wait until later in the evening to talk with her husband about the matter, but now would have to be the time. "I start as soon as we can get Gertie situated."

"Situated?"

"Yes," answered Angie nervously. "The senior care center called me today. She got loose again and they had to call the police."

"Oh, no," he moaned and collapsed into a chair.

"And there have been other incidents." Taking her time, Angie carefully explained each incident to her husband, including the evaluation by Dr. Simmons. "Martha Smith informed me today that they would no longer be able to care for Gertie."

"Oh, brother," exclaimed Paul. "What now?"

"Paul," she responded, taking his hand. "I think it's time we begin looking for a home for Gertie."

"A nursing home!" he exclaimed, leaping to his feet. "No way is my mother going to one of those death houses!"

"Paul," she countered. "They're not death houses. Some of those homes are very lovely and provide great care."

"My mother would never want to go to a nursing home."

"How do you know, Paul?"

"She told me so several years ago when we were visiting one of her friends at a nursing home. She said she'd never want to live in one of those homes. She said if it came down to it, just to shoot her."

"That was before the dementia."

"We can take care of her ourselves. In our own home."

"We," exclaimed Angie. "Exactly who is the 'we' in this plan of yours?"

"I'll help."

"When it's convenient. You're too busy at work. You barely have time to mow the yard once a week. Paul, I'm the 'we' and you know it."

"Is that so bad?"

"Paul," she said, softening her voice. "I've been offered a wonderful job. I'm going to be very busy myself. It's my turn. How would you like it if you had to quit your job to take care of Gertie?"

"That's ridiculous. I'll be making three times the money you'll make starting out."

"Then the bottom line is that I have to put my life on hold again."

"We'll hire a nurse."

"They're too expensive and too unreliable. Besides, we'd have to hire two nurses to cover our schedules."

"With your salary and our savings we can hire help."

"My salary and our savings are going for Jim's tuition."

"He could go to the community college."

"No!" shouted Angie. "No way! Jim worked hard to get into Northwestern. He deserves to go. And, right behind him is Cheryl."

"Well," countered Paul. "If that's the case how the hell are we going to afford a nursing home? Mom doesn't have any money."

"I've already considered that," said Angie. "She'll have to go on welfare."

"What?" gasped Paul. "My mother on welfare."

"I know how it sounds but most families whose parents don't have money register them for welfare. Think about it. A nursing home costs over $30,000 per year. Dr. Simmons says Gertie could live for another twenty years. We'd be bankrupted."

"No way," shouted Paul as he grabbed his jacket and headed out the back door. "No way!" She heard him repeat as the car door slammed shut.

It was after seven when she heard the car pull into the driveway. Paul entered through the back door and sat at the kitchen table. He looked defeated. Angie pulled a chair up to the table. "I know this is hard, dear. But we have to face reality."

"Reality," he snorted, laughing softly.

"You find this funny?" asked Angie, confused.

"No, no," he quickly replied. "It's just the concept of reality."

"I don't understand."

"No, you couldn't understand because I haven't been completely honest with you," admitted Paul. "I was going to tell you. I was just looking for the right time. It seems as if Gertie has forced a lot of truth telling on us."

"Paul," said Angie, reaching for his hand.

"You know I've always had a desire to find out about my real father. Gertie told me he died at Auschwitz just before the war ended. I was about three when we immigrated to America. She met Bill, married him, and that was the end of Dad. At least it was for her. I tried to get more information from her, but she always replied that she didn't want to talk about it. They were horrible memories and she wanted to leave them in the past. I should have listened, but I didn't. I was obsessed. The few times that I traveled to Europe on business, I always took an extra day to travel to Auschwitz and some of the other camps. I talked with people, walked the sites, searched records, but could find nothing. Then, a month ago I was at work when I received a phone call from overseas. It was a woman named Eddie Goldstein. She was referred to me by a gentleman I met at one of the camps. In a conversation, he mentioned that he had spoken with an American that was in search of his father. He mentioned my mother's name and camp. Apparently this woman was at the same camp and indicated that her best friend's name there was Gertie. She called wondering if it could be the same person. I faxed a picture of my mother to her."

"Oh, my God," gasped Angie. "You found your father?"

Paul's shoulders slumped. "No, worse, I lost my mother."

"I don't understand," said Angie.

The man reached for his wife's hand. "Angie, Gertie is not my mother."

"How is that possible?"

"According to Eddie, this is what happened." Paul paused to gather his composure. "Under the rules of the camp, she was allowed to keep one and only one child with her. She had two children, me and a sister I never knew I had. When they arrived at the camp the word spread quickly among the women. My mother realized that one of us would be taken from her and without an adult guardian, death was a certainty. According to Edith Goldstein, my mother pleaded with the childless women around her to take one of her children. No one would."

"Why?" asked Angie.

"A woman with a child took risks in the camp. It was difficult enough to survive by yourself. It was even harder with a child."

"Oh, God."

"At the last moment, when an SS officer asked if the two children belonged to my mother, Gertie reached forward and grabbed my hand and pulled me to her. She told the officer I was her child. At first, the officer didn't believe her. But Gertie was adamant and wouldn't relent. In the end, the officer let her keep me."

"And your mother?"

"She and Gertie were separated. My mother and sister were assigned to one part of the camp. Gertie and I were herded to another. According to Eddie, all of the people assigned to my mother's group were eventually exterminated. I don't know what Gertie did or how she managed it, but we were among the few survivors. After the war, she simply claimed me as her natural son. It was easy since the Nazis destroyed everyone's paperwork. We immigrated to America and that was end of the story."

"And Gertie's kept the secret all these years?"

"Yes," nodded Paul. "I'm not sure even Bill knew the story."

"Are you going to tell her you know?"

"Absolutely not," stated Paul. "In her mind, I'm her son. That's the way she wanted it and that's the way it'll end." He wiped the tears that had pooled in his eyes. "That's why I can't send her to a nursing home."

"Paul," she pleaded. "I understand how you feel. But we are still left with the problem. We can't hire private nurses and we can't ask the kids to put their lives on hold. And you can't quit your job. We'd never survive on my salary."

"I know, I know," he muttered. Taking her hand he stoked it gently. "I know it's a lot to ask, Angie, but I was hoping maybe you could find a small part-time job for the time being and we could keep mom at home with us. It's where she belongs."

Angie looked away from her husband to the large kitchen window. The sun had set now. What little light remained was slowly being extinguished by a veil of darkness approaching from the east. In the background, she could faintly hear the words of her husband as he detailed the choice he wanted her to make. Like her dreams, the words grew more and more faint.

Angie's Day   Name_____

Instructions: read each statement before coming to class. Indicate your response by circling "agree" or "disagree" at the end of the statement. In class, discuss the statement with your group and attempt to reach consensus. If consensus is impossible record your vote and write *your* individual response to the statement in three or more complete sentences.

1. After saving Paul's life, Gertie has the right to live in his home for the rest of her life. Agree or Disagree. **Group Vote: Agree_____ Disagree _____**

2. Angie doesn't really have a choice, she has to give up her dreams and care for Gertie. Agree or Disagree. **Group Vote: Agree_____ Disagree _____**

3. This is Paul's problem, not Angie's, he should give up his job to care for Gertie. Agree or Disagree. **Group Vote: Agree_____ Disagree _____**

4. In marriage, women have all the responsibilities and men have all the privileges. Agree or Disagree. **Group Vote: Agree_____ Disagree _____**

5. If Gertie goes to the nursing home it only makes sense to put her on welfare. Agree or Disagree. **Group Vote: Agree_____ Disagree _____**

6. Nursing homes are just another way of not dealing with the responsibilities of family. Agree or Disagree. **Group Vote: Agree_____ Disagree_____**

7. It's not fair that Paul and Angie's son has to forego attending a selective college in order to help care for Gertie. Agree or Disagree. **Group Vote: Agree_____ Disagree_____**

8. If Paul is forced to send Gertie to a nursing home, irreparable damage will be done to the marriage. Agree or Disagree. **Group Vote: Agree_____ Disagree_____**

9. The real problem in this case is that the government has not provided enough assistance to the elderly in society. Agree or Disagree. **Group Vote: Agree_____ Disagree _____**

10. This is a generational issue. Young women today would not be in this situation. Agree or Disagree. **Group Vote: Agree_____ Disagree_____**

Question # 1: If you were Angie, what would you do? Why? Be sure to use information and theory from your textbook to support your decision.

_____
_____
_____
_____
_____
_____
_____
_____
_____
_____
_____
_____
_____
_____
_____
_____
_____
_____
_____
_____
_____
_____
_____
_____
_____
_____
_____
_____

Question # 2: Caring for the elderly has become a major problem in society. What programs might government offer to help alleviate the problem? If your suggestions result in more spending, detail where the government will obtain the funds.

Brothers

There was something about the black '70 Chevelle that made him feel calm no matter how uptight he was. Walking toward it, he looked at its clean lines. The gleam pleased his eyes as the slick, glossy surface caught the sunshine. The tense knots in his neck and shoulders eased as soon as he touched the smooth finish, slightly warm from the struggling April sun. It was easy to forget his demanding father and bitchy mother and all of the damn problems he had waiting to assault him at any moment. The minute he popped the door and slid into contours of the well-worn leather bucket seat, he was home. And when the door closed behind and he slid the key into the ignition and turned over the 454 big block, life belonged to him again. The radio popped on automatically, of course. If Zeppelin happened to be jammin', he knew he couldn't lose.

Jesus. You'd think the only thing in the entire world was school and grades and work. He wished the old broad would get off his back! He couldn't even stay in his damn room without her hassling him. If only he could afford to move out. One more year at school, if he got lucky and his grades held. Then, he was history. Outta here.

The car wasn't running, Josh was just sitting in it, listening to music, parked on the driveway. He thought about the first time he saw it, and how much work and time and money he'd sunk into it over the past four years. But damn, it was worth it. Hell, it was more than worth it! Every one of his friends agreed that he had the best-ever wheels.

The only thing missing now was a nice, cold beer. Jesus. You'd never know he'd turned 21 two weeks ago. It might as well have never happened. The eagle-eyed old bitch still wouldn't let him sneak a beer out of the house anyway. You'd think Dad was counting the cans or something. He couldn't wait until later when the guys came around. He knew they'd end up by the old mill in the cemetery. The best place around for having a few beers on a Friday night. He might even let the little guy come along. Yeah! That might be fun. After all, he'd be celebrating his 18th birthday this week. Why not?

It was weird. All of his friends hated their punky little brothers. But he and Jim had always gotten along well. Sometimes he treated Jim like a jerk. But that was mostly when his buddies were around. And he always made up for it later. Jim was 3 years and 2 weeks younger, but that didn't seem to matter. He couldn't explain it, but from the time they were small, they were always pals and took care of each other. Always. And just because he was older didn't mean that Jim hadn't saved his butt more than a time or two. Yeah, you could always count on the little guy.

Yeah. Tonight they were going to the old mill. In fact, just he and old Jimbo were going to go. They hadn't done anything alone together since the camping trip last fall.

Josh yanked the key, popped the door, and got out of the car. He walked backwards for a few steps and admired the old girl. He opened up the trunk and checked to make sure that the cooler was still there. Yep. Still there. Getting beer was no longer a problem, thank God. He thought back over all of the scrapes he'd gotten into over the past few years. Most of them involved either his car or beer, or both. Josh slammed the trunk lid shut. He headed back to the house. Once inside, he made a few phone calls to tell the guys he wasn't available tonight. Then he took a nap.

Jim was stuck in the long line of cars trying to get the hell out of the parking lot. Friday afternoon, 4 p.m. and everyone was dying to get out. The black 1968 Camaro SS's stock 350 engine was running hotter than it should have been. Another thing he was going to have to check into his weekend. Damn! He wished he had Josh's touch with cars. Hell, he wished he cared as much about the SS as Josh cared about his old Chevelle. Jim had owned this car for three months and there was still so much to do.

He wanted to paint it and make it look good, but Josh said no way. First the inside. Then the outside. Hell, he was probably right.

Looking to his right he noticed Andy Caine, waiting to turn right in the lane next to him. "Hey man," he shouted, "we're meeting at Kim's house at 8. Be there!"

Andy flashed him a peace sign. What a throwback! You'd think this was the '60s for God's sake. Jim wondered what would happen to the three guys he'd been hanging with since grade school. Here it was, the last couple of months of high school and those three jerks had no idea what they wanted to do with their lives. At least Andy was sort-of planning to attend the community college in their area. But Ben and Mike were just goof-offs. They thought they'd move in together when their parents kicked them out. Yeah, sure. Neither of those two jerks had ever had a decent job. Hell, neither of them stayed at any job long enough to get anywhere. They both quit as soon as the least thing went wrong.

Not Jim. He'd had the same job at the Ice House that Josh had gotten for him when he turned 16. UIC had accepted him right off the bat. He planned to live at home, work at the Ice House, and after four years walk away from UIC with a degree in Computer Science and start out making 50K a year.

Jim laughed as he finally maneuvered the SS into the street. How did he ever end up with Ben and Mike as friends? Even a bigger question: how did he ever end up with Josh for a brother? Oh, Josh was the best. No question. Jim knew he'd do anything for his big brother. But Josh had his problems. School problems, home problems, girl problems, even police problems. Mom kept telling him he was making her an old woman. And he probably was.

Jim thought about his mom. She was looking a bit wrecked these days. She kept telling Josh that as much as she loved him, it was a good thing she had at least one good kid. Jim guessed that all of the crap that Josh put the old lady through was tough to take. Josh and he could laugh about it, but Jim had heard his mom crying in her room after the last police incident.

How did Josh always end up being at the wrong place at the wrong time? He got away with nothing! He'd probably get arrested for jaywalking.

He pulled up onto the driveway. Yep, definitely running hot. First thing in the morning that was going to have to get fixed.

Walking into the house he tossed the keys onto the kitchen table and went to the stove to see what his mom was cooking.

"Hi kiddo. Tough day? Homework?" His mom always talked in shortcuts.

"Hi Mom. No homework. It's April, it's Friday, and I'm a senior. I hope to never do homework again until the fall when I start UIC."

Mom drew a heavy sigh and closed her eyes. "Not you, too. I don't think I can take it. Don't mess things up now."

"For God's sakes, Mom. I've been accepted! Relax. Nothing matters." Sometimes she definitely was a nag. "When can I eat the chili? I'm starved and we're all going out later so I need a nap and a shower."

"You are going nowhere later, little guy." Josh was standing in the doorway.

"Hey! Big guy, I am definitely going out later." Jim and Josh had done this big guy/little guy thing for years. Of course, now Jim was just a little taller so he should have been the big guy. On the other hand, Josh still had him all out if you were counting bulk. Jim was a scrawny 6'2 to Josh's bulky 6'1. Both towered over their "little mom" but shared her blue eyes and blond hair. It was impossible to miss that they were brothers.

"Sorry, dude, but you're going with me. I need your help. OK?"

Jim caught his brother's look and suspected that the big guy was once again in trouble. Now what? "No sweat. I'll make some calls."

Jim wandered out of the kitchen but heard his mom's voice and stopped. "Eat anytime, guys. It's on the stove and hot. Dad won't be in until very late and I'm taking this opportunity to lock myself into my room to relax with a good book." She paused and then continued, "Josh, no trouble, do you hear? Whatever it is that you have planned with Jim, there had better not be any problems. You know, your father is going to kill you if you even think about...."

"Yeah, yeah, yeah. I hear you. This has nothing to do with trouble. We just need to go to a friend's house and work on a car. Relax mom, you're gonna go crazy if you don't relax."

"That's why I'm trying to go to my room. I just want to make sure that there will be no panic phone calls at midnight. All I want is peace, quiet, and tranquility. Please, Josh," she turned to look at her older son, "I need that." Then, she quickly moved out of the kitchen and headed down the hall to her room. Both of her sons watched her go and waited until they heard her bedroom door click shut.

"So, what's the deal, big guy?" Jim finally had the chance to ask his brother what was going on. After a nap and a shower, he felt up to whatever his big brother's problem might be.

"No, problem. You and I are going to celebrate your birthday. That's all."

Jim spooned some chili into his mouth and looked up. "Are you serious? What'd you have in mind?"

"Just meet me at the cemetery in an hour. That's all you need to know." Josh was smiling as he disappeared out of the back door and and a minute later Jim heard the sweet purr of the Chevelle.

Hours later, they left the cemetery together after a few beers to celebrate Jim's upcoming birthday. The Chevelle was in the lead. Jim was clutching the wheel for all he was worth. Good old Josh had never been second at anything. Both brothers were a little buzzed. Not under. Just a little high.

The SS overtook the Chevelle at the intersection. Jim couldn't believe that Josh would let him catch up like that! Jim flipped Josh off as he passed him and let out a joyful yell, "Yehaw!"

Josh laughed. He knew his car could take the little SS anytime, anywhere. He squeezed the accelerator lovingly and torqued the wheel gently as he passed his little brother in the long, dark, straightaway stretch. Once passed, he knew he could leave Jimbo in a cloud of dust.

Josh checked the rearview mirror to see how much distance there was between himself and the headlights of Jimbo's car. Where was the little guy? The bump jarred him and he turned his eyes back to the road in front of him. Damned potholes! Where was that jerk?

After the long mile on the dark straightaway, Josh turned the corner and headed up towards his own street. Within minutes, he was parked on his driveway. He waited awhile. No Jimbo.

Jim watched the Chevelle's brake lights flash in the distance. Shit! He might as well not try. Let him go. Instead, he decided to stop by and see if the party was still going at Kim's house. He hit the brakes, made a u-ie in the middle of the highway, and headed in the opposite direction.

The next morning Jim ambled into the kitchen, rumpled white tee shirt and sleepy eyes. Josh was at the table toying with a bowl of cereal.

"Hey man. Looking a little peaked there, big guy."

"Jim, where did you get to last night? One minute you were behind me and the next minute you were gone."

"I knew I couldn't catch you and I wanted to check out Kim's house."

"Did you go to the party?"

"No," he replied casually. "I guess by the time I got there, they'd moved it someplace else. I was tired and decided to just come home and hit the rack."

"Did you come home past the cemetery?" Josh's voice sounded like gravel.

"Naw. I took the Interstate. I don't like revisiting points of my humiliation. Listen, just cause you beat me...."

"Then you don't know." Josh cut him off. Jim noticed that he was looking really sick. Josh said, "They're looking for an older model, black, racing style car. The one that hit Jeff Jackson. Up by Millers. And took off."

The meaning of his brother's words sank in and Jim grabbed the back of the kitchen chair. "Oh, my God! Josh, you gotta believe me, man. I never hit anyone! Let's go look at my car. Oh, my God. Could I have hit someone and not know?" Jim sank down into the chair. The meaning of what had happened was all over him. Could he have killed someone?

"I'm going out to look at my car. If you hit someone, there's gotta be something on the car." Jim got to his feet unsteadily and headed for the door.

Josh grabbed at his brother's arm and held on tight. "You don't have to look, man. It wasn't you. It was me."

The two brothers stared at each other. Both felt sick and responsible and terrified. Jim's voice shook. "Josh! How could have hit someone and left? Was he dead? How bad is your car?"

"Shit. I never knew I hit him! It was only 10:30, but I came straight home and parked up on the driveway. I was waiting for you. I got out of the car and went to dump the ice out of the cooler. When I walked around the front, the overhead floodlight was shining on the bumper. There was a smear of what I thought was mud. I was gonna clean it up, but I was pissed 'cause you disappeared so I figured I'd hit the hay and wash it tomorrow. I was asleep for about an hour when the phone rang. I grabbed it before mom heard it. I thought it was you and you were in trouble or something. It was Eric telling me they found Jeff up by Millers. As he was talking, I suddenly knew. I got ice cold all over and thought I was gonna puke. I remembered hitting a pothole just about the time I was cruising past Millers. After I hung up the phone, I went back outside. I took the flashlight and a wet rag. When I got outside and looked, I knew for sure. I'd hit Jeff. I wiped some blood and hair off the bumper." Josh stopped and shuddered at the memory. "It was just on the chrome. There weren't any other marks anywhere. I used the chamois to wipe everything evenly. I snuck down to the basement, dumped everything into the washing machine with soap and bleach. Then I waited, threw it into the dryer, and put it all away. Like it never happened. Then I went to my room and spent the night thinking about the fact that I killed someone!"

Staring at Josh, Jim got up and went to check out the cars. He almost expected to find his car dented and smeared with blood. But nothing. Neither car looked even a little guilty. They both sat in the sunlight and sparkled.

Images of Jeff Jackson rapid fired through his mind. He was an only child, a good guy, and since the death of his father had worked hard to support his mother. What would Mrs. Jackson do now, he wondered. She would be devastated, emotionally and financially. He felt a hand on his shoulder. He turned to see Josh, tears on his cheeks.

"Jim," he pleaded softly. "I'm gonna need your help. They may not have my plate number from the accident, but they know my car. They'll be coming around. You've got to alibi for me, say we were together someplace else, like the beach, no drinking."

"But Josh," he muttered. "Your insurance. You're fully covered. Mrs. Jackson's gonna need the help. Hell, she'll never make it without Jeff."

"Jim," begged his older brother. "I'm an adult with two priors. If they find out, I'm gonna do jail time, no question about it. Think about mom, Jim. It'll kill her, you know it will. I'm gonna clean-up my act, trust me. You've gotta believe me. We're brothers, Jim...."

Jim stood looking at the cars. The sunlight skimming off the hot shinny metal blinded him and he turned away to avoid the glare and wondered if he could turn a blind eye to what his brother had done.

Brothers   Name _____

Instructions: read each statement before coming to class. Indicate your response by circling "agree" or "disagree" at the end of the statement. In class, discuss the statement with your group and attempt to reach consensus. If consensus is impossible record your vote and write *your* individual response to the statement in three or more complete sentences.

1. Josh should just wait to see what happens. Maybe he'll never be caught and the whole thing will go away. Agree or Disagree. **Group Vote: Agree_____ Disagree _____**

2. Jim should take his brother's fall. Nothing will happen to him because he is underage with no priors, but Josh is definitely going to jail. Agree or Disagree. **Group Vote: Agree_____ Disagree _____**

3. Jim should go to the police if Josh doesn't. He knows a crime has been committed and he is honor bound to tell the truth. Agree or Disagree. **Group Vote: Agree_____ Disagree _____**

4. Anyone caught drinking and driving should go to jail regardless of the circumstances. Agree or Disagree. **Group Vote: Agree_____ Disagree _____**

5. If you locked up everyone who has ever driven after "a few too many," two-thirds of the population would do jail time. Agree or Disagree. **Group Vote: Agree_____ Disagree _____**

6. The most important thing in life is family. Therefore, Jim needs to stick with his brother. Agree or Disagree. **Group Vote: Agree_____ Disagree_____**

7. Jim's moral obligation to Mrs. Jackson outweighs his responsibility to his brother. Agree or Disagree. **Group Vote: Agree_____ Disagree_____**

8. Josh deserves another chance since he has vowed to turn his life around. Agree or Disagree. **Group Vote: Agree_____ Disagree_____**

9. Serving jail time for this crime will only destroy Josh's life. Nothing positive will come of it. Agree or Disagree. **Group Vote: Agree_____ Disagree _____**

10. If Jim doesn't turn Josh in to the police, he is as guilty as his brother. Agree or Disagree. **Group Vote: Agree_____ Disagree_____**

Question #1: If you were Jim, what would you do? Why? Be sure to use information and theory from your textbook to support your decision.

Question # 2: Do you believe that jail time is an effective deterrent for drinking and driving? If so, why? If not, what suggestions do you have for alternative punishments?

Ernesto's Legacy

Ernesto Ricardo walked briskly along O'Sullivan Boulevard. The day was warm and filled with sunshine. Above, the bank marquee informed passersby what they were well aware of—it was hot—92 degrees. Stepping under an awning to seek momentary relief from the heat, the young man paused. He had given himself ample time to reach his destination and to collect his thoughts before his interview. Watching those passing by he was struck with the realization that of the tens of thousands of pedestrians who walked this street daily, few if any, were aware of the man for whom the street was named. Ernesto, however, was well aquatinted with the man and his legend. As the city's fourth fire chief, Daniel J. O'Sullivan was credited with standing up to the corrupt politicians who used fire fighter's jobs to curry political favors among friends, relatives, and campaign workers. Before O'Sullivan rose to the position of chief, the city's fire department was a veritable wasteland of incompetence and fraud. Counting on O'Sullivan to continue the practice, the city politicians appointed him to the post after the death of his predecessor. O'Sullivan proved to be a major disappointment to city hall. Once appointed he moved swiftly, firing those lacking in credentials, commitment, or knowledge of modern fire-fighting methods. Similar action was taken to replace political appointments on the review commission charged with the responsibility of new hires. In their place he appointed community individuals with experience, vision, and a reputation for honesty. When the politicians balked, he threatened to go public with information on bribes and ghost-workers tied directly to the city council. Threats soon followed and in the following months O'Sullivan was twice shot in thinly veiled robbery attempts. However, he survived and so did his hopes for a model fire department worthy of national praise.

Yes, thought Ernesto, O'Sullivan was a true hero, the type of fire fighter he would model himself after. And soon, very soon, he would be given the chance to begin his career. Of this he was sure. Less than four weeks ago he had taken the fire fighters examination and felt confident that he had done well. Then, only days ago, the cherished letter arrived in the mail notifying him to appear before the review board this very afternoon for an interview. He couldn't remember a time in his life that he had felt such joy. He telephoned his wife at work to share the news and she immediately began calling all the relatives to inform them of their good fortune. That night they had shared a special meal and explained to their five year-old son that daddy was soon going to be a fire fighter. The child's face lit up and he began circling the room pretending to drive a fire truck while making high pitched siren noises.

Ernesto checked his watch. He wanted to be sure that he would arrive on time. Stepping out from under the canopy, he headed toward his destination. Along the way he contemplated his circumstances.

Life had been hard. Ernesto had arrived in this country as a young boy when his family emigrated from Cuba to escape tyranny and poverty. His father was certain that life would be better in America. During the perilous journey in their small boat his father had explained to him why they were leaving their homeland. *"America,"* he shouted over crashing waves, *"de las oportunidades!"* Ernesto knew little of this. But his father assured him and the family that they would find their fortune in this new land.

At first, Ramon Ricardo's vision seemed prophetic. Within months of their arrival the president and Congress, sympathetic to the plight of Cubans, had granted them official legal status, thus clearing the way for citizenship. *"America!"* proclaimed his exuberant father once again, *"de las oportunidades!"*

It would be the last of such proclamations.

In Cuba, Ernesto's father had been a gifted mason. His work was well known and his skill much sought after. However, in American, he soon found that talent alone was not enough. Whereas in Cuba the politicians controlled the destiny of one's life, in America a tangled web of unionism and cronyism dominated. From job site to job site, Ernesto's father traveled in search of work. With him he carried pictures of his work in Cuba as evidence of his craftsmanship. In each case he was informed—no union card, no work!

"Why does one have to have a card to work," he shouted to his family, "this is America!"

Finally, after months of searching he relented and trudged down to the union hall where he encountered an older man with a thick neck, a sagging belly, and a wrinkled face. Scratching his unshaven chin the man looked at pictures of Ramon's work and tossed them back across the table. "So," the man muttered contemptuously.

"They are good, are they not?" inquired Ernesto's father in broken English.

"They'll pass," admitted the man, swatting a fly.

"Pass," cried Ernesto's father. "What does this mean, pass? My work is *magnifico*. In Cuba, I was *numero uno!* Fidel Castro himself sought my skill."

The older man's face suddenly turned solemn. Picking up his pencil he quickly began writing, repeating the words as he wrote. "Ramon Ricardo, recommended by Fidel Casto." With that, the men in the office began howling with laughter.

Intense heat spread across Ramon's face as anger and embarrassment engulfed him. He prayed silently to the Blessed Virgin Mary for composure. Then, he calmly pleaded, "It is true. I am new to this country of yours. But, my work is good and I need money to support my family."

"That's better," oozed the older man with the satisfaction of knowing that he had gotten on top of the immigrant. "Respect is important in this line of work." Reaching under the table the man withdrew a new application form and handed it to Ramon. "Fill this out and bring it back."

Ramon took the form and turned to the door before being stopped by the man who, with a wiggle of his stubby index finger, motioned for him to return to the desk. Whispering, so that Ramon had to lean over the desktop to hear, the man said, "Now, I should also tell you that when you return your application you'll need to bring in a processing fee."

"A processing fee?" asked Ramon. "How much is this processing fee?"

Taking out a sheet of paper the man scribbled a figure on it and slid it across the desktop to Ramon.

"A thousand dollars!" cried Ramon.

The man shushed him quickly. "Look," he said, "it's not mandatory. You don't have to pay. It's just that most people who get their cards pay."

"What does this processing fee do?"

"It's a kinda consulting fee. You pay it to us and we help you with your application. Make sure it's filled out properly—t's are crossed and the i's dotted. Know what I mean?" the man said with a wink.

Ramon knew exactly what he meant. He understood that without the fee, he would not get his union card. He desperately wanted to tell the man what he thought of him, but without the card his family would suffer. He swallowed his pride, thanked the man, and informed him that he would return in the morning.

That evening Ramon discussed the situation with his wife. There was, of course, no money to give to the man. Their only possessions of any monetary worth were a few pieces of his wife's jewelry that had been handed down through several generations. Without hesitation, Maria opened her jewelry box and handed the contents to Ramon. He protested, but she said that the jewels were worth nothing in comparison to the family's future. The following morning Ramon took them to a jewelry dealer and though he was paid a fraction of their true value, it was sufficient to cover the processing fee. Later that morning, he took his application and the processing fee to the union office. The older man with thick hands took him to a back room where he looked over the application. Then, after pocketing the fee, the man filled out a union card with Ramon's name on it and handed it to him along with instructions on where to report in the morning for work assignments.

Although perturbed at the indignity he had suffered, Ramon tried to put the incident behind him reasoning that better times were ahead. That night he proudly displayed his new union card as the family celebrated with a special meal prepared by his wife. Though happy to have the card, he felt embarrassed at having been responsible for the loss of his wife's prized jewelry. As the family ate, Ramon silently bargained with himself. He would begin work tomorrow and when he did they would see his work and appreciate his skill. In no time he would be making lots of money and with that money he would buy his beloved Maria new jewels that would make the ones he had sold look insignificant in comparison.

Ramon was up early the following morning. He dressed quickly and headed off to the union shop to receive his work assignment. When he arrived, he found many other men waiting. At seven sharp, a man stepped to the desk in front of the room and began to read names and handing out job assignments. Ramon's name was not among those called. Racing up to the desk, Ramon inquired as to why his name was not called. Reaching into his pocket, he withdrew the union card and handed it to the man.

The man studied the card for a moment and then shrugged. "Okay, you've got a union card. So what?"

"I have the card, I get the work," replied Ramon.

"No," huffed the man. "That's not the way it works. Lots of people have cards. Everyone here has a card. That doesn't guarantee you work. It only means that you're in the union."

"I don't understand," replied Ramon anxiously.

"What it means is that we work on a seniority system here. You got your card yesterday. You're the low man on the ladder. You have to wait your turn."

"But I have a family," cried Ramon. "I must work!"

The man flipped through the pages attached to a clipboard he carried. "So you want work."

"Yes," replied Ramon quickly.

"I've a job on 37th street that needs a jobber."

"A jobber?" asked Ramon unfamiliar with the term.

"Yes, a jobber," replied the man. "You'll mix the concrete and carry the stones to the brickers."

"That is work for a *peon*!" cried Ramon. "I am a mason."

"Whatever," said the man. "It's all I have. Take it or leave it. I don't give a damn one way or the other."

Again Ramon felt the heat spread across his face. How could he accept this work? How could he not? "I will take the work," Ramon finally said.

"Good move," replied the man as he handed the assignment to Ramon. "Better get started, the brickers are gonna be wanting their materials soon."

When Ramon appeared at the job site, he handed his paperwork to the man the others said was the foreman. Minutes later he was mixing concrete and carrying the heavy stones. As he worked he noticed that all of the jobbers were Hispanic, all of the brickers were white. During the break, he spoke to the other jobbers and informed them of his plight. They only laughed. When Ramon asked what was so funny, one man replied, "Amigo, don't be so foolish. You're a jobber. You will always be a jobber. To be a mason you must be white. It is the way it works."

"But I have a card."

With that the men laughed again. Afterwards, they explained to Ramon how the system worked. Yes, there was a union. And yes, there was the seniority system. Then, there was the real system, the one in the back room, the gringos' room. It was there, they told him, where they decided who worked and who didn't. It was the unwritten rule, they explained— masons will be white; jobbers will be Mexican.

"But I am Cuban," protested Ramon.

"Amigo," stated the man who had explained to Ramon how the system worked. "To the gringo, you're just another spic."

"What is the meaning of this word spic?" inquired Ramon.

As the men explained, a knot began to develop in the pit of his stomach. How was he going to explain this to Maria? What of their dreams? Could it be true, what these men said? Ramon cautioned himself not to believe the hurtful words of the men. After all, none of them possessed a card as he did. He would work today and tomorrow would be different.

The following day Ramon showed up for work only to find that, again, there was no mason's work for him. Again, as he did the entire week, he worked as a jobber. Following work on Friday he made his way back to the union office to complain. The union chief indicated that he would inquire into the matter. On Monday, when Ramon showed up for his work assignment there was no work for him, not even that of a jobber. Immediately, he went to see the union chief who told him that the foreman had complained that his work was not sufficient. Ramon protested, "I am the hardest worker of all the men!" The union chief simply shook his head explaining that jobbers were not covered by union rules. It was entirely up to the contractors.

Ramon left the building and began walking the streets. He finally understood. The others had been right. Ramon would not be a mason and by complaining he had lost his work as a jobber. Tears welled up in his eyes. What had he done to deserve this injustice? How would he support his Maria and the children? Along the way he saw a help wanted sign posted in the window of a restaurant. Entering the restaurant, Ramon talked with the owner. The job was for a bus boy. Humiliation engulfed him. He wanted to turn and walk away but his pockets were empty and Maria needed to go to the store for food.

From then on, Ramon bused his tables and kept his thoughts to himself. Occasionally, his mind would drift to his dream of resuming his work as a mason. But, as the years passed, he began to realize it was only a dream. One day, as he was making his way home after work, Ramon was killed while crossing a street. The driver of the car had been drinking and according to one witness, a street person, was driving erratically. However, no ticket was issued, perhaps due to the man's political connections. The police disposition was that it was simply an unfortunate accident. In fact, they suggested that Ramon was to blame for the accident by crossing the intersection before the light had turned. Although this was contrary to the eyewitness' account, the police disregarded that testimony as unreliable. In a civil suit, a jury awarded less than $60,000 in damages to Maria and the family. Maria's attorney explained to her that the award was so small due to the lack of negligence on the part of the driver and the fact that compensatory settlements are based on the victim's expected lifetime earnings. As a bus boy, Ramon's family could hardly expect much. In fact, the attorney stated, they were lucky to have received what they did. After the attorney deducted his one-third from the settlement, little money was left. It was then that Ernesto dropped out of high school and began working to support the family.

As he walked to his meeting, Ernesto contemplated his life. Yes, it was true that he'd had little choice in dropping out of school. But then it wasn't much of a school.

Each class had forty or more students to a room and, in the whole building, there was only one outdated computer. Although there were a few good teachers, most were overworked, underpaid, or simply passing time until retirement. It was not the type of school where a teacher wanted to begin a career. Nevertheless, it was where his dream was forged. In the eighth grade, firemen had visited the school and talked to the children. Ernesto was infatuated with the men and their uniforms. Remembering his father's fate, Ernesto had asked if someone like him could be a fire fighter. In response, a fire fighter told the story of Daniel O'Sullivan and how he had ended corruption and cronyism. He assured Ernesto that with hard work and determination he could one day become a fire fighter. From that day, Ernesto never deviated from his dream, even after he had dropped out of school to help support his family. When he met and married Alona, he continued his studies. At nineteen he sat for and passed the GED and obtained his high school degree. After the birth of his son, he continued to study independently whenever he could. When available, he would work overtime and that money would be put into what he and Alona called, the dream jar. When enough had been accumulated, he would take the money out to pay tuition for a course at the community college. He was preparing himself for the fire examination given every seven years. By the time the exam was given, Ernesto, now 25, had accumulated enough college credit to qualify. He felt confident after taking the exam and now, after all the hard work, he was ready to become a fire fighter.

Ernesto arrived for his meeting ten minutes early. He gave his name to the receptionist and was instructed to take a seat. On the opposite side of the room sat another young man. From what Ernesto could approximate, he appeared to be about the same age as himself. He was tall with sandy red hair and broad shoulders. Perhaps, thought Ernesto, he too would become a fire fighter. As the young man looked up Ernesto smiled. The young man returned the smile. Ernesto thought about striking up a conversation with him, but he was too nervous. It would be better, he reasoned, to concentrate on what he would say to the review board.

Inside the room, five men and two women debated loudly and with each comment the discussion grew more heated.

"What the hell are we even doing here?" shouted Duffy Gray, a man in his fifties with a pitted complexion and a balding head. "We have the scores. We know Jeremy Madden is the best candidate."

"No," shouted Linda Evans, an African American woman in her late thirties. "We know that Jeremy's score on the examination is slightly better than Ernesto's. We don't know who the best candidate is. The test tells us both young men are qualified. That's why we're going to interview them both today."

"Look," shot Bill Houstin, a tall, rail-thin man with flinty eyes, "Duffy's right. The other candidates were selected on who had the best test scores. It's not right to change the rules for the last opening."

"We're not changing the rules," countered Gary Hill who sat to the right of Linda. He was a man in his late twenties with a shock of blondish hair. "We're just saying that maybe in this case special consideration needs to be given to Ernesto Ricardo."

"Bull!" screamed Gray. "That's all that affirmative action crap! We're running a fire department here, not a social welfare agency."

"Duffy's right," spoke Bill Houstin before anyone could reply. "Peoples lives are at stake here. We need to select only the best. Besides," he offered, "we already have a minority on the department."

"A minority," cried Linda Evans. "You have one token black fire fighter out of forty and you think that's reasonable?"

"Hey," countered Houstin, "he's not a token. He earned his position like everyone else—by the book."

"Maybe," commented Gary Hill, "it's time to change the book."

With Hill's comment the room exploded. Dennis Mackavich sat quietly, contemplating the arguments on both sides. Of everyone, he was the only member of the review board who had not made up his mind as to which candidate would be chosen for the last position. He had suggested the selection of both candidates, but city hall was adamant, the budget would not support an additional position. They would have to choose. And it was painfully obvious to him that he would have to cast the deciding vote. Amidst the rancorous haggling he quietly stood up and waited for calm. The gesture finally brought the others to silence. "All of this settles nothing. We have invited these two men to appear before the review board. They are outside waiting. I suggest we get on with it."

The others grudgingly agreed and the first candidate, Ernesto Ricardo, was ushered into the room. For the next forty minutes Ernesto answered a wide variety of questions about his education, his work, and related interests. Linda Evans, much to the displeasure of Houstin and Gray, asked Ernesto to recount the events of his family life and the difficulties they had encountered in coming to America. Ernesto was clearly uncomfortable with the discussion of such matters, but nevertheless complied. When the interview was over, Ernesto thanked the members of the committee for the opportunity to meet with them and indicated that he looked forward to joining the team.

"What a great young man," comment Hill after Ernesto had left.

"Do you think," said Houstin sarcastically, "that it would be appropriate to interview the other candidate before making up your mind?"

"I didn't..." began Hill, before being interrupted by Dennis Mackavich. "Let's not start again. Let's move forward."

With that, Jeremy Madden was asked to step into the room and Duffy Gray began the discussion. "Jeremy, tell us why you would like to become a fire fighter."

The young man leaned forward in his chair. He ran his fingers through his thick hair. "I've always wanted to be a fire fighter. As you know from my records, my grandfather was a fire fighter. As a child he told me stories of the fires he fought and the lives he saved." The young man laughed nervously. "I think my parent thought my wanting to be a fire fighter was a childhood fantasy, but it wasn't. They understand that now. When I received my baccalaureate degree I could have gone into business. I think that's what my father would have preferred, but it wasn't for me. I've really never had any doubts about becoming a fire fighter."

"And your father supports your decision now?" asked Houstin.

"Very much so. I finally convinced him that for me to be happy I have to follow my own dream."

"Is it the excitement that attracts you to the profession?" asked Hill.

"I would be less than honest if I said no," admitted Jeremy. "But it's more than excitement. I look upon it as the opportunity to help others. Please don't misunderstand. I'm no Mother Theresa, but I believe that you can find happiness in helping others."

"It says here in your resume that you are proficient with computers. You list quite a number of programs you're capable of running."

"Yes," admitted Jeremy. "I learned a lot about computers from my father. Then, when I was sixteen, my grandfather passed away and left me some money. I bought a state-of-the-art computer along with a number of powerful software programs."

"I would have thought that at sixteen you'd go out and buy a new car with that money," mused Houstin.

"It crossed my mind," laughed Jeremy. "But I figured the car could come later. My future was more important."

"Commendable," muttered Grey just loud enough so that the others could hear.

The interview lasted a few minutes more and then Jeremy was dismissed and told to join Ernesto in the waiting room.

After the door had closed, Hill was the first to speak. "That settles it. I'm voting for Jeremy."

"Me, too," chimed Houstin. "He has the better scores and all the computer skills. It isn't even close."

"Com' on," cried Linda Evans. "Did you even listen to Ernesto's life story?"

"I did," stated the man curtly. "He's got a sad story. But so what?"

"So what?" cried the woman leaping from her chair.

"Yeah, so what?" repeated Houstin. "Lots of people have sad stories. You think my parents came to this country on the Queen Elizabeth? They came here with nothing, took their knocks on the streets, and made their way up the ladder just like other immigrants. And they did it without whining about the social injustices."

"Please," injected Mackavich standing again. Linda Evans sat back down. The room grew still.

It was Gray who spoke. "From the looks of it, we're deadlocked. Bill and I are voting for Jeremy. Linda and Gary are voting for Ernesto. It's your call Dennis. You're the deciding vote. You have to go out and shake the hand of one and tell the other one to go home. Who's it gonna be?"

Dennis Mackavich looked up from the table. On the wall across the room hung a picture of Daniel J. O'Sullivan, the man Ernesto had admired in his interview. He too had similar feelings. In a perilous time of corruption and violence, O'Sullivan had stepped forward to sever the ties binding the department to corruption and political cronyism. He was a beacon of hope in a time of darkness. In place of political patronage he had established tests and guidelines to select fire fighters. Gray and Houstin argued vehemently to preserve the current practice maintaining that affirmative action or special consideration was just another form of political patronage. Evans and Hill disagreed. From their vantage, the current method of selection was biased against minorities and the poor and, in essence, was just another form of patronage clothed in the linens of righteousness. Looking up at the picture he wondered what O'Sullivan would do if he were here today. He closed his eyes. He was aware of the voices of those in the room who had resumed their arguments. As the voices faded, words and images blended into a translucent picture of reality. Rising from his chair he walked to the door....

Ernesto's Legacy   Name_____

Instructions: read each statement before coming to class. Indicate your response by circling "agree" or "disagree" at the end of the statement. In class discuss the statement with your group and attempt to reach consensus. If consensus is impossible record your vote and write *your* individual response to the statement in three or more complete sentences.

1. The American educational system treats everyone fairly. Agree or Disagree. **Group Vote:** **Agree_____ Disagree _____**

2. Anyone can make it in America if they work hard and long enough. Agree or Disagree. **Group Vote: Agree_____ Disagree _____**

3. In life, it's who you know, not what you know, that counts. Agree or Disagree. **Group Vote: Agree_____ Disagree _____**

4. Affirmative action might have been useful at one time, but with the recent strides in race relations in this country it is an outdated concept. Agree or Disagree. **Group Vote: Agree_____ Disagree _____**

5. The educational system is deliberately designed to promote the interest of the affluent in our society. Agree or Disagree. **Group Vote: Agree_____ Disagree _____**

6. Just because there is only one black fire fighter on a department of forty, does not mean the department is guilty of discrimination.   Agree or Disagree.   **Group Vote: Agree_____   Disagree_____**

7. Jeremy had better scores than Ernesto. Therefore, he will make the better fire fighter.   Agree or Disagree. **Group Vote: Agree_____   Disagree_____**

8. It's not fair to penalize Jeremy just because his parents could afford to send him to better schools. Agree or Disagree. **Group Vote: Agree_____   Disagree_____**

9. Affirmative action is just another term for "reverse discrimination." Agree or Disagree. **Group Vote: Agree_____   Disagree _____**

10. Without affirmative action, it's impossible for minorities to get ahead in society. Agree or Disagree. **Group Vote: Agree_____   Disagree_____**

Question #1: If you were Dennis Mackavich, which candidate would you vote for? Why? Be sure to use information and theory from your textbook to support your decision.

Question # 2: Do you believe affirmative action is still necessary in our society? Be sure to list the reasons for your answer.

Fallen Star

Lee dreaded going back into the conference room to face his nemesis. He'd washed his hands and face and combed his hair after relieving himself in the plush gray and maroon executive bathroom. Now it was time to pull himself together and face Jo Ward in her lair. He had to let her know what his final decision was going to be. Even after a sleepless night filled with conscious decision making and the performance of numerous cost-benefit analyses, he still felt unsure of what he wanted to do and how he would handle the outcome. Would he go along with Jo's plan or would he choose to defy her? Actually, he wanted to run and hide, of course, but since that wasn't an option and he was faced with making a forced-choice decision, he felt anxious. His stomach was queasy with the fear that grabs you when you know your entire life may well be on the line.

Despite himself, Lee had to smile. How ironic it was that decision-making had been the skill that had gotten him hired at Altwell and Brandeis in the first place. Had it really been nine years since he was let go after the hostile takeover of his old company? Yeah, the good old days. For whatever reason, Lee, who had been so successful at his old job, was never quite able to pull off the coups that had gotten him the reputation as most promising young executive at the old place. Since arriving at A&B, Lee had, of course, had his successes. But it was nothing like it had been in the early years when he was straight out of college.

Now, at 40, Lee had been forced to swallow the bitter pill of being passed over for several promotions, a sure sign that he had reached the peak and would be stuck somewhere in the middle of the proverbial company ladder. In his youth he had often imagined, no dreamed, of what it was like at the top. He no longer entertained that thought since it had become obvious that he would never reach those dizzying heights. He had become used to watching younger and greener men and women pluck prize plums from the tree of executive assignments. A&B dangled them tantalizingly in front of those individuals sharp enough and lucky enough to successfully launch and win an important campaign. He had often seen executives with less talent succeed and rocket to monetary victory. Over the years he had noticed though, that these lucky few usually possessed a quality that a top-level company mentor valued. It seemed the only way to compete for prized positions was by latching onto a rising, and better yet risen, star.

Lee couldn't resist smirking at the serious face that stared back at him from the mirror. Yes, there he was. Gray suited, blue tied, and gracefully aging with just the correct company haircut and with the prerequisite number of silver strands located strategically at his temples to give him just the perfect image of company drone. The only thing that was missing was the slight smile centrally located on his serious face. Instead, there was the smirk.

He tore himself away from the mocking image, straightened his shoulders and then turned on the heel of his perfectly polished wing tipped shoe. He wasn't wholly sure of what he'd say, or even what he'd do, but he knew that the time had come to do it now.

Jo Ward was the only female vice president that A&B had, and at A&B being a VP was third best only to being President and God, in that order. Jo had held her hard earned position for over a decade and had every intention of holding onto it until she became President. She aspired to the God title but realized that even she had some limitations.

The perks that went along with being a VP at A&B were countless and the limits pretty much included the sky. Jo had traveled the world, lived in luxuriously appointed condos and hotels, was waited upon by the best body slaves and house servants, and demanded the utmost in all situations and settings. At 50—slim, very attractive, and extremely well kept—she was used to asking, actually demanding, and receiving instantly, if not sooner. But even VP Jo Ward had the inevitable list of the unattainable things that seems to come automatically with life. The list was, granted, a very short list, but it did, none-the-less, exist. Once a day, usually just about the time that she opened her eyes in the morning, she reviewed that list to remind herself of the importance of keeping her edge. Among the items that had over the years eluded her grasp, there was only one name, and he was from a long, long time ago. Jo had no intention of allowing Lee Hanley to add his name to that list.

She looked out from the wall of windows onto the glistening silver lake below. From the luxurious rooftop office located along Chicago's gold coast she watched the waves of Lake Michigan crash repeatedly onto the beige, sandy beach. The sun shone almost painfully bright and she imagined the sweltering heat outside on the unprotected sidewalks that gave access to the smart and ritzy shops located along the street. The thought made her warm even in the perfectly climate-controlled office. That, along with the heat produced by her erotic thoughts about Lee, made droplets of sweat appear on her upper lip and pool between her perfectly sculpted, silk-caressed breasts.

Jo couldn't remember a time when she desired any one as much as she wanted Lee. She wasn't quite sure what to make of it all and at first had tried to repress her intense feelings of lust. She had reminded herself that Lee was not worthy of her attention. True, he was intensely attractive and adequately intelligent, but after nine years she knew he had no place in the company hierarchy. That, in and of itself, should have been more than enough to chill her heat. But it wasn't. And that was how she had come to the point of offering him, and in the process herself, this one last chance.

It was the best of everything. He would get what he had always wanted. She did not consider herself unfair. A chance he'd never be given under ordinary circumstances. A chance that she, as his mentor, could provide for him. And she, in return, would get what she needed—a chance to work out some of her sexual frustrations on his beautiful lean body; a chance to quench the thirst she felt for the man; a chance to relieve some stress and relax. A chance to spend a few days at perfect rest.

And then, best of all, a chance to get rid of him, to banish him physically and mentally from her life. Best for both of them that he disappear from Chicago and she could get back to concentrating on her work in an uninterrupted fashion.

But what had happened when she had offered him this incredible deal? He had had the nerve to turn her down! Without sensitivity, without a touch of class, without so much as a second of hesitation. He hadn't even tried to spare her feelings. He had just blundered along with his stupid "no way" adolescent attitude. Well, that was just another acquittal of how right she was, along with all the other company moguls, in not having promoted him.

Yet, all of this did not cause the heat she felt for Lee to desist. On the contrary, she now felt the need to possess him, to make him acquiesce, to bend his will to hers, more urgently than ever. So, she had called him to her office and left him standing in silence while she lay back sensually in her plush chair, crossed her silky legs and allowing the soft material of her expensive designer suit to drape provocatively across her breasts while she pointedly looked him over. She let him see just enough of her long legs to offer incentive. Then, after just the right amount of time had passed to make him feel maximally uncomfortable, with her hands tented, thumbs resting just above her breasts, she made him an offer he couldn't possible refuse.

The company meeting in Hawaii at the end of the month would include appointment announcements made by the directing VP's. She needed to announce her choice for the head of the Southern branch of A&B. If Lee chose to accompany her, it would mean that he would be sharing her suite, her bed, and she would in turn announce that he would be named Branch Manger of A&B South for the next three years. Long enough for Lee to make the name for himself that he coveted. Or fail. Whichever. It didn't much matter to Jo. In companies like A&B, middle of the road executives like Lee Hanley came and went.

Jo made what she wanted from Lee crystal clear. In return for this nomination, she expected that he would turn her inside out for as often and as long as she chose for the duration of the Hawaii trip. Three days of sex, cozy dinners, and one short meeting handing him the plum that he had been competing for and had no chance in hell of getting on his own.

And at the end of the trip she would be flying off to work in Paris for six weeks while Lee packed up his Chicago office and settled in Chattanooga. The two would meet seldom and then only on a business basis. Unless of course, and Jo suspected that this would happen, Lee called her for an occasional private meeting. Simple, easy, and good for all concerned. How could he go wrong?

Lee whipped open the bathroom door and started down the long corridor. What choices were there anyway? To refuse would mean trying to start over at forty without a first rate recommendation. Everything was against him. His age, the economy, his track record at A&B. Without a decent recommendation, it would be impossible. Could he survive? To accept would mean the position that he had always hoped and worked for would be his. He would finally prove himself to all concerned. But it would also mean that probably everyone in the company would know that he had slept his way to the position. Furthermore, he would have to live with the knowledge that he had sold himself for a job.

And what about Cindy? Did his wife have the right to participate in this decision? He had considered telling her about the bind he was in but then decided against involving her for the usual reasons. He almost laughed trying to picture himself telling Cindy that he had to screw Jo Ward to keep his job. It really was laughable. Here he was in a situation other men would kill for. It wasn't as if he was some type of vestal virgin either. He thought back on that time years ago when he had becom involved with his secretary. He had thought about leaving Cindy then. Now, in this situation, he felt dirty and used and worst of all, trapped.

Then there was Kimmy. At thirteen, she had the right to a bright future living the life she had been raised to appreciate. Going to the right schools and wearing the right clothes had become as important to her as tennis lessons and summer trips to Disney World and winter ski breaks. Did he have the right to jeopardize her future? What if he refused and then was jobless for God knew how many months, maybe years?

Who should I sell out? Myself? My job? My family? Then the next question is where does it end? What if Jo demands more and won't let me be? What if Cindy finds out?

The elevator bell pinged softly and the big doors slid silently open. Lee stepped into the ascending cage and stared dumbly at the buttons on the side panel. Up to the conference room to announce his decision to sell himself for a job? Or down to his office? If he chose down, there was no need to turn Jo down. He didn't need to face her. He just needed to pack his things and walk. The only question was—where to?

Name_____

Instructions: read each statement before coming to class. Indicate your response by circling "agree" or "disagree" at the end of the statement. In class, discuss the statement with your group and attempt to reach consensus. If consensus is impossible record your vote and write *your* individual response to the statement in three or more complete sentences.

1. Sexual norms and behaviors are different for men than they are for women. Agree or Disagree.
    Group Vote: Agree_____ Disagree _____

2. Refusing Jo's offer will financially devastate the family. Lee should have sex with Jo for the benefit of his family. Agree or Disagree. **Group Vote: Agree_____ Disagree _____**

3. It would be much harder for a man to prove sexual harassment than it would be for a woman. Agree or Disagree. **Group Vote: Agree_____ Disagree _____**

4. If Lee does agree to sexual relations with Jo, he should not feel guilty since he had little choice. Agree or Disagree. **Group Vote: Agree_____ Disagree _____**

5. Since men view sex differently than do women, it would probably be easier for Lee to have sex with Jo than it would be for his wife to have sex with her boss. Agree or Disagree. **Group Vote: Agree_____ Disagree _____**

6. Lee should tell his wife about the offer from Jo and let her make the decision. Agree or Disagree.
   Group Vote: Agree_____ Disagree_____

7. Unless you're willing to bend a little, you'll never make it in the corporate world. Agree or Disagree.
   Group Vote: Agree_____ Disagree_____

8. You can't fault Jo for making an advance on Lee. After all, men have been doing it to women since the beginning of time. Agree or Disagree. **Group Vote: Agree_____ Disagree_____**

9. People make all kinds of moral concessions in business. This is a minor one in comparison to those that hurt other employees and consumers. Agree or Disagree. **Group Vote: Agree_____ Disagree _____**

10. Suing for sexual harassment will only result in Lee being labeled a troublemaker, thus making it impossible for him to find another job. Agree or Disagree. **Group Vote: Agree_____ Disagree_____**

Question # 1: If you were Lee, what would you do? Why? Be sure to use information and theory from your textbook to support your decision.

Question # 2: In your opinion, do you believe that sexual attitudes and norms in the workplace have changed in the last few decades? If so, list some reasons for this change.

Fly Boys

She bent low over the filthy cot so that the frail child could see her face. Prior to her visit, the hospital aid had explained that the disease ravaged the muscles of the eyes making it difficult to focus. The young girl was little more than a skeleton, an emaciated body waiting for death's relief.

The child's eyes blinked several times before recognizing the figure hovering over her. Her lips parted slightly in a vain attempt to smile. Amidst the inflamed gums, only a few teeth remained. That mattered little however, as the child's appetite had deserted her days earlier. When the woman inquired why she was not being fed intravenously, the nurse shrugged as she swept her arms around the expanse of the crowded hospital before replying, "Why would we do that? Without medicine there is no hope. Why torture the child? She will die and then another will be brought in to occupy the bed. There are many, many more. The lucky ones, like this little one here, will have a clean bed in which to die."

The frail arm, a long slender bone wrapped loosely in wrinkled, tissue-thin skin reached up. "She wants to touch your hair," explained the nurse. "It's superstition among the villagers. To touch the hair of a princess brings good fortune." The woman bent lower turning her head slightly so that her long silvery hair hung loose. She felt the soft touch of the child's hand slide gently over her hair. Reaching down, she took the child's hand in hers, and slowly combed the frail bony fingers though her silvery strands.

65

The child uttered an unfamiliar phrase. "What did she say, Sister?"

"She expresses her gratitude for making her passage to the next world easier," replied the nun.

Tears pooled in the woman's eyes. She wanted to respond, but could not for fear of freeing the emotions within her. Now was not the time to display weakness. She needed to be strong so that the child could draw strength from her. Quickly, she took a breath and choked back a mournful wail surging up her throat. In an attempt to gain composure, she closed her eyes and sternly castigated herself for her weakness. Then smiling, she gently brushed the child's withered cheek. Turning, she slowly walked the aisle leading to the outside world. A world none of these children would visit again.

Ella Steavers paced the floor of the oval office. Her shoulder length silver hair swayed back and forth as she spoke. John Steavers, her husband and the president of the United States, listened intently. A week ago, he had sent Ella on a fact-finding mission to ascertain the medical crisis facing the African continent. She was a brilliant woman with an extraordinary ability to discern fact from fiction, truth from fantasy. He trusted her explicitly and had relied heavily on her opinion throughout his first term. God only knew that with all of the sharks continuously circling him he needed someone to keep the lifeboat afloat. On more than one occasion Ella's intuitive abilities had averted disaster. He smiled now as he watched her animated form pace the floor.

"What?" she asked, stopping.

"Nothing," he quickly replied.

"Don't tell me nothing, " she countered. "You're smiling. You haven't heard a word I've said."

"I have," he protested before smiling again. "It's just that I've never seen you so emotionally involved in an issue."

She stood still, staring hard at her husband.

"Ella," he protested. "I can't go to Congress with anecdotal stories of poor kids dying. Sure, they'll feel bad, but sympathy alone is not going to move them to open the purse strings of the treasury to all of Africa."

The woman took a deep breath and then exhaled slowly. "Okay, John," she said stoically as she opened her briefcase and withdrew a pile of papers, "You want facts, let's talk facts."

The president smiled again. He was about to receive a lecture from the only person on the face of the earth capable of delivering one to him. It would be straightforward, concise, and accurate down to the slightest detail. And, it would be delivered without an interruption. He watched her flip through the papers until she came upon a set bound together by a large red clip. Seeing the clip the president knew that these would be the all-important notes. His wife always used a red metal clip for the most important papers. She took a brief moment to peruse the notes. "Ready, John?"

"For you, Ella, always," he replied with a wink.

The woman's expression suddenly turned gravely serious. "If you're preoccupied with other matters perhaps we should wait until a more opportune moment to address this."

"No Ella," he quickly replied. "I was. . ."

"Look, John," she interrupted. "I didn't ask to go to Africa. You came to me, remember? You said you were serious and you wanted an honest assessment. Maybe that was not the case. Maybe you're playing to the African American vote in preparation for your re-election bid."

"You know me better than that, Ella," he protested. "It's true that I've been getting pressure to do something about the health crisis in Africa from the minority caucus in Congress, but my intentions are honest. You should know that about me, Ella," he paused to study her eyes. "How serious is it?" he finally asked.

"The worst, John. It simply is beyond imagination. It's so bad that it's almost impossible to put it into words to convey the desperation of the people."

"Tell me."

"Unless we take immediate action, Africa will be lost." Sensing the possibility of disbelief over such a grandiose statement she added, "this is not an exaggeration, John. Twenty-three million Africans are living with AIDS. If you compute that as a percentage of all AIDS victims in the world, over 70 percent are Africans. As of now, over 13 million Africans have died of AIDS. Again, in comparative figures it means that 90 percent of all global AIDS deaths are African." Ella paused to let her husband contemplate the numbers.

"And it gets worse. Projections by United Nations health officials estimate that in five years the total number of AIDS patients in Africa will reach 20 million. Think of the numbers," she implored. "With all the medical achievement of modern society this epidemic will surpass the bubonic plague of Medieval Europe."

"Is this true of all of Africa?" he asked.

"As expected, it varies country to country and there are ethnic variations. For example, the Zulu of South Africa have a 30 percent infection rate. It's estimated that over 40 percent of them will die in the next decade. Most of the victims are women and children."

Ella paused. She flipped a page. "Think about this, in Johannesburg General Hospital in South Africa, a modern country by our standards, 75 percent of all infant deaths are related to AIDS. Fully one-third of all South African women who visit rape clinics test positive for AIDS. In Zimbabwe, over 60 percent of hospital beds are occupied by AIDS victims. And, with population shifts due to war and famine it's impossible for any one nation not to be affected."

"How does a country function with that kind of AIDS rate?" asked the president.

"That's the second part of this whole nightmare. The medical crisis is so great that the fragile economies of these nations are about to collapse. Here's just a few examples," she said flipping to another page. "In Zimbabwe, agriculture fields stand barren because tens of thousands of farmers are infected and unable to work. This, of course, leads to famine, more deaths, and migrations to other nations by infected populations. In Zambia, an oil refinery recently went bankrupt due to AIDS-related costs of workers' medical care and burial fees. In South Africa, 45 percent of the mine workers are affected and productivity is escalating downward at an alarming rate. That's only a sample of what's on the horizon for these economies!" she finally exclaimed. "John, we have to respond. And we have to do it now!"

"But, Ella, the problem is so big. Think about the billions it would cost the American taxpayers."

It was now time for the woman to smile. "That's the beauty of it all, John. It won't cost a dime."

An expression of puzzlement crossed the president's face.

"It's true," she quickly replied. "I've had numerous conversations with leaders all across Africa. They have a solution."

"Exactly what is this solution," asked the president warily.

"They want the freedom to manufacture drugs developed in the west for use by their people. They want to do it without interference from U.S. pharmaceutical companies that hold the patents on the drugs. All they want is assurance from you that you will not impose a trade embargo on them for copyright infringement. They can manufacture the drugs at a fraction of the cost and distribute them to the poor who are most infected and have no means to pay for treatment. Then, in the future, when the crisis is under control and the economies are on solid ground, they will discontinue production. It's the perfect solution. The only solution."

The president shifted in his chair as he softly muttered, "The American taxpayers save money; the continent is salvaged, and African nations help themselves. Can it be this easy?"

"It can, John. In fact, it's the only solution that will work. And it works for the world, not just for the Africans. It helps them rebuild their economies and that will improve global economics."

"Okay," he said, springing up. "We'll call it the 'African Initiative.' Let's get to work!"

A week later, late at night as the president was getting ready to retire, his chief of staff, Velma Johnson, called. The president lifted the phone reluctantly, perturbed at the interruption.

"Mr. President," she said. "We've got problems on your African Initiative."

"How so?" he inquired. "I ran it by the congressional leadership and the black caucus. Everyone's on board."

"Not anymore. Everyone in Congress, with the exception of the black caucus, is running for the tall grass."

"Why?"

"A tidal wave of lobbyists hit capital hill today," she answered. "They swarmed the place."

"Who?" asked the president. "Who are they?"

"You name it—lobbyists representing Biotech firms, pharmaceutical companies, Wall Street brokerage companies, Chambers of Commerce, the medical community. Even the unions have people twisting arms. I've never seen the likes of it. It's intense and it's united."

The president rubbed his weary eyes. "Okay, what now?"

"I've spoken to the congressional leaders on both sides. They're insisting that you hear what the lobbyists have to say."

"Line it up as soon as possible," directed the president. "The sooner we take care of this, the sooner we can move forward."

Two days later a diverse group of lobbyists assembled in the Oval Office. The president greeted each guest personally, shaking hands and making light conversation in an attempt to build a positive atmosphere for the discourse that was to follow.

Finishing the last greeting, the president sat down. "Ladies and gentlemen, I hear you have some objections to the African Initiative. I'm here to listen to your concerns."

Paul Stare, president of Biotech First, one of the largest research firms in biochemistry, was first to speak. "Frankly, Mr. President, we are appalled and alarmed at this initiative of yours. And in saying so I think that I speak for all of us here today." With that a murmur of approval registered around the room.

"What could possibly be wrong with it?" asked the president.

"On the surface it all seems very humanitarian. And I suspect that there are members in your own party, particularly among the black caucus in Congress, that support it. But, in reality it would be disastrous to the interest of this country."

"How?" questioned the president.

Sandra Evans representing the pharmaceutical companies spoke up. "In essence it's a violation of international agreements on copyright and patent infringements. These medicines are the creation of private companies. Essentially you're giving approval for others to steal from us."

"But millions are dying," countered the president.

"But millions are saved by upholding copyright and patent laws."

An expression of puzzlement spread across the president's face.

"Maybe I can help," offered Paul Stare. "What Sandra is saying is that the current system, as unfair as it might seem to the poor, will actually save more lives than what you are proposing."

"How can that be?" asked the president.

"It's simple economics. Each new drug we develop costs in the neighborhood of five hundred million dollars. I know that seems like a lot, but think of the cost we face in research and development. These miracle drugs don't fall into our laps. It takes years of painstaking research and development. And, there are no guarantees. Most projects end in failure and the loss of millions of dollars. That's why when we do succeed we have to capitalize big time in order to cover losses and provide dollars for future research. It's the only way we stay in business. Allowing the African nations to infringe on our patents will destroy us."

"I don't see how," admitted the president.

"It's about investment money," continue Paul Stare. "People look at the pharmaceutical companies like a rich uncle with unlimited money. But in reality, our money comes from ordinary citizens who invest in our stock, hoping to make a profit. Allowing nations to manufacture our drugs without compensation deprives our stockholders of profits. When that happens, our stockholders will dump us for more lucrative investments. We'll lose billions and with it the ability to pursue new research. Without the private sector, the only medical research in this country will be that sponsored by the federal government and we both know that's a drop in the bucket."

"Perhaps I can provide another perspective," chimed in Anna Parker from the medical association. "The drugs themselves are not the answer for several reasons. First and foremost is the need of the African communities affected to change lifestyle and cultural attitudes. In the countries most affected with AIDS one sees a clear pattern of poverty, overpopulation, promiscuity, and unprotected sex. In those countries not affected as heavily you see a different picture—governments engaged in educational programs and more responsible behavior. Allowing free access to Western medicines will, in some ways, actually exacerbate the problem."

The president shifted in his chair. Again, a puzzled expression crossed his face.

Anna Parker continued immediately. "Giving medicine would only provide a false sense of security to the people. They would lose any incentive to change the behaviors that created the problem. Likewise, the governments of these nations would not be forced to make tough decisions. In those countries most affected by AIDS the government spends between one and ten dollars per person per year on medical care. Most of the money goes to corrupt officials and weapons to fight ethnic wars. One of the harshest lessons we've learned in providing medical supplies to these countries is that often the government quickly confiscates the supplies for their soldier's use or sells them on the black market for cash. The people who are most in need never see the medical supplies we provide. And finally, even if we did give our medicines away, drugs are not going to be effective because the people lack the skills and education to use them properly. This is a lesson we learned with antibiotics. For example, penicillin is distributed openly on the street. People take it when they're not even sick in the mistaken belief that it will help them ward off diseases like AIDS. And, they take it sporadically, a day or two at a time. This allows bacteria and viruses to mutate to drug resistant strains. In effect, they're destroying our antibiotic sources faster than we can create new ones."

"So you can see, Mr. President," Paul Stare said after a moment of silence, "that the answer is not in destroying our own medical industries. Africa's problems are deeply rooted in their own governments and traditions. We cannot solve Africa's problems. Africa must solve its own problems."

James Wilson, from the National Chamber of Commerce, was next to speak. "Mr. President, our concern is more global. We fight counterfeiting of products all over the world. Allowing African nations to counterfeit medical patents will send a message that we lack the will to enforce the law. You can't selectively allow counterfeiting in one industry and not expect it to affect others. Besides, how do you enforce medical patents in Asia or South America when you allow the Africans to pirate them free of charge? The whole world will demand the same treatment we afford to the African nations. It'll be disastrous."

Ella Steavers was attending a global conference on human rights when word reached her of the president's meeting. In tune with the changing tides of politics, she quickly boarded her personal jet and returned to Washington, D.C.

Three hours later she entered the oval office to find her husband and his chief of staff, Velma Johnson, working at a small table. The president rose to greet her but she quickly skirted around him. "Rumor has it, John, that you're backing off the African Initiative."

"Let's say we're taking a second look at it's potential consequences."

"Then it's true. They got to you."

"That's not fair, Ella," he countered. "Sit down and let me tell you the other side." For an hour the president recounted the objections raised by the lobbyists in the meeting she had missed.

"Fly boys," muttered the president's wife. "It's all about fly boys."

"Fly boys," repeated the president. "What the hell are fly boys and what do they have to do with what we're talking about?"

The woman sat next to her husband. "In the old colonial days the British hired fly boys to protect themselves against tsetse flies that carried sleeping sickness. The tsetse fly harbored a wormlike, one-celled parasite called a trypanosome. A bite by an infected fly would deposit the parasite into the circulatory system where it would worm its way to the victim's brain and it triggered trembling, lethargy, erratic behavior and finally, a comma leading to death. It can kill its victim in a matter of weeks. Anyway, the British hired young African boys to go stand by the open bush areas. To attract the flies, the boys would remove their shirt and a partner, another boy, would attempt to swat the fly before it could bite. The British paid the boys a bounty for each fly they killed."

"Good heavens," exclaimed the president in horror.

"That's the point of all of this. Our meddling, our exploitation of the African people produced these problems. Western mining, logging, and farming conglomerates have tapped into the hardships of these people as a cheap labor source to accumulate vast fortunes. Men are transported to isolated regions where they work for months at a time with no contact from family members. What would expect to happen? Deprived of their wives, they seek the services of prostitutes which, I might add, Western businesses are only too happy to provide to keep workers content and working. When the men do return home, they pass the disease to their wives. In other cases, Western corporations are pushing their workers deeper into the forests where these microbes exist. And, when the workers get sick, the company abandons them. Compounding the problem is famine which has forced millions to poach in remote areas for food. Where were the relief agencies when they were needed? Do you think we'd stand by and let a western nation suffer the way we have some countries in Africa? So who's to blame?" She paused for a moment and then concluded. "John, the world's getting smaller and smaller. It's no longer possible to isolate Africa from the rest of the world. With global transportation and immigration the problems of Africa become the world's problems. Sooner or later it's going to sweep across the ocean to our shores."

The president contemplated the arguments and then spoke. "I agree. We have to act. Tomorrow, I'm announcing that we will not invoke sanctions against African nations seeking to manufacture and distribute medicines to fight this terrible epidemic." Velma Johnson began to protest but the president held up his hand for silence. "The decision is made. In time everyone will see that it was the right one. Thank you for your advice."

Two weeks passed and the president assembled a team of international health officials, foreign policy analysts, scientists, engineers, and logistic experts to begin working out the details of providing the knowledge and technology to put his plan into action. On Wednesday of the third week following the decision, the president was approached by Velma Johnson. An assembly of House and Senate members from his own political party had requested a conference. When he inquired about the agenda for the meeting, the president was informed that it was in reference to his African Initiative. At first, he balked but was persuaded that it would be difficult to refuse a request from his own party members. The meeting was set for the following afternoon where sixteen influential members of the president's party along with several citizens where in attendance.

"Okay, Bob," began the president speaking to the most senior member, "what's on your mind?"

"The African Initative," came the reply.

"Bob," he stated firmly, "the decision has been made."

"We realize that," said the man. "We need to broadened the program."

The president smiled. "I'm glad you understand. I need your support on this. The pharmaceutical companies and every business organization down the line has been raising hell over it. We need to stick together."

The senior congressman rubbed his forehead. "Mr. President, I don't think you understand. What we would like is for you to expand the program so that American citizens will receive the same benefits as do African citizens."

"What?" the president asked anxiously.

"It's simple, Mr. President. If African citizens get medications for free, then so should Americans." The man paused and looked to his right where the three citizens sat together. "Sir, I'd like you to meet Jerry Stefovich. He has a story I think you should hear."

The president nodded and smiled. He felt trapped, with little choice.

"Mr. President," Stefovich began. "I just want you to know that I voted for you in the last election. It was my opinion that you were an honest and caring man. I hope to vote for you in the next election."

"Mr. Stefovich," encouraged the congressman in a soft voice, "please tell the president what you told me."

"Well," he began, "the bottom line, and I do mean the bottom line, is that I'm broke. I should say my wife, Ella, and I are broke. Busted flat out. It wasn't always that way. We worked hard, the both of us. Ella worked in a diner in Piedmont Springs and I was a pipe fitter. We didn't make a fortune but we worked hard, bought a house, saved for the kids' education, and still managed to put a little nest egg away for retirement. Things were going pretty well. Hell," he said and then stopped, his face red. "Can I say that here?"

"Don't worry," smiled the president, "you ought to hear some of the language world leaders use when they get excited."

"Well, as I was saying," he began again, "things were okay. We were doing pretty well for ordinary folk. We were proud of ourselves. Then Lizzi came home from college, sick. She went to one of them damn fraternity parties. Some kid slipped something into her drink and the next thing she knew she was having sex with some boy she didn't even know. Turns out the kid had AIDS. Lizzi got real sick. At first, the insurance company paid, but then we hit our limit. Man, those hospitals and drugs are expensive. After that, we went to the county aid department. I didn't want to, but you do what you have to do. They told us they couldn't help on account of the money we had in the house and the nest egg. They said you had to be poor, without resources, to get help. Well, we sold the house and Ella's car. Then, we used the nest egg. We took out some credit cards and borrowed on them. I know we shouldn't have done that, but we were desperate. We needed to keep Lizzi alive. Now, we're on welfare. Lizzi gets some treatment, but not what she really needs." The man paused to regain his composure. "Well, when I heard about your new program for Africans, I called up my representative, Bob here," he said, pointing to the senior politician. "I got to thinking that since we developed and paid for it through all the profits the drug industry collects off of us Americans, we should be entitled to the same benefits. Everyone of us here has the same story, Mr. President. If you do see your way clear on this it won't bring back my house or the money me and Ella saved, but it would help Lizzi. And maybe other Americans won't have to have their lives ruined if something happens to them like what happed to us. It seems only fair, doesn't it Mr. President?"

Fly Boys   Name_____

Instructions: read each statement before coming to class. Indicate your response by circling "agree" or "disagree" at the end of the statement. In class, discuss the statement with your group and attempt to reach consensus. If consensus is impossible record your vote and write *your* individual response to the statement in three or more complete sentences.

1. The money America spends on foreign nations could be better spent on its own people. Agree or Disagree. **Group Vote: Agree_____   Disagree _____**

2. Giving aid to African nations won't help alleviate suffering, it will only line the pockets of corrupt politicians. Agree or Disagree. **Group Vote: Agree_____   Disagree _____**

3. It's unfair and illegal for the president of the United States not to enforce patent and copyright laws. Agree or Disagree. **Group Vote: Agree_____   Disagree _____**

4. Allowing African nations to produce AIDS medications without compensation is really cheating American citizens who have invested in the stock of pharmaceutical companies. Agree or Disagree. **Group Vote: Agree_____   Disagree _____**

5. The real problem of AIDS in Africa is ignorance, superstition, and the promiscuous lifestlyes of its people. Agree or Disagree. **Group Vote: Agree_____   Disagree _____**

6. The African Initiative will seriously damage the president's chances for reelection. Agree or Disagree. **Group Vote: Agree_____ Disagree_____**

7. Jerry Stefovich is right, it's unfair to bankrupt American citizens for AIDS treatment and then give it away to Africans. Agree or Disagree. **Group Vote: Agree_____ Disagree_____**

8. Once Africa receives the right to produce AIDS medication without payment to American pharmaceutical companies, all third world nations will demand the same privilege. Agree or Disagree. **Group Vote: Agree_____ Disagree_____**

9. The only reason we have been able to develop our medical technology is because investors are willing to buy pharmaceutical stocks. The African Initiative is bound to scare investors away and damage the future of medical research. Agree or Disagree. **Group Vote: Agree_____ Disagree _____**

10. With global travel and immigration, it would be foolish not to help African nations with their medical problems. Agree or Disagree. **Group Vote: Agree_____ Disagree_____**

Question # 1: If you were President Steavers, would you allow African nations to manufacture AIDS medications without payment to the pharmaceutical companies?

_____
_____
_____
_____
_____
_____
_____
_____
_____
_____
_____
_____
_____
_____
_____
_____
_____
_____
_____
_____
_____
_____
_____
_____
_____
_____
_____
_____
_____
_____
_____
_____
_____

Question # 2: If you were President Steavers, would you provide AIDS medications to the citizens of America for free?

_____

_____

_____

_____

_____

_____

_____

_____

_____

_____

_____

_____

_____

_____

_____

_____

_____

_____

_____

_____

_____

_____

_____

_____

_____

_____

_____

_____

_____

_____

_____

_____

_____

_____

Habit

The snow was swirling around the dark ground in a wild dance. It was ice-cold and the only warm thing about Jim was the glowing tip of the cigarette anchored firmly between the index and middle finger of his right hand. He was freezing, but this was the only chance he'd have for the next two hours to grab a desperately needed quick smoke.

Damn! Damn, damn, damn. How did they get away with this? Weren't at least half of the people on campus smokers? In May when he left school there were places all over where smokers could go for a break to grab a quick cigarette. Now, every place inside was smoke free. He felt like a little kid who was not allowed to smoke inside the house. This was crazy. He couldn't remember feeling so frustrated. Quickly, he spun around, flicked the butt out into the dark, and went back inside.

Linda couldn't deny it. She was going through Jim's drawers trying to find where he hid the smokes. His jacket reeked of cigarettes, but he always had excuses. He couldn't help it if his friends smoked! John smoked. And Ryan smoked. Jim didn't smoke. But Linda didn't quite believe him. In her heart, she knew that her son was lying to her.

Finally she gave up. No cigarettes, anywhere. She couldn't decide if she was happy or angry. And then, when she turned around, there they were. Big as life, bold as you can dream! The corner of the red box, right underneath his pillow on his bed. She grabbed the pack and ran triumphantly to the kitchen. She had been right! She was vindicated! Now, it was just a question of getting him to stop. Suddenly, she had a sobering thought—just exactly how was she going to accomplish that? How does one person make another person stop smoking? She picked up the phone to break the news to her husband.

Together, the couple was trying to decide just how to handle it. He was for confrontation and absolute insistence on quitting immediately. She was thinking aloud about "the patch" or hypnosis or even ear piercing to help him stop. She wanted to keep talking about the negative side effects. Maybe they should enroll him in a clinic program to get rid of the monkey on his back. The discussion was still grave and at odds an hour later. Jim was almost due home and no decision had been made.

Jim was singing when he walked into the house after class. The song died on his lips when he saw the look on the faces of his parents.

"Guys. What's up? Someone die or something?"

Habit   Name_____

Instructions: read each statement before coming to class. Indicate your response by circling "agree" or "disagree" at the end of the statement. In class, discuss the statement with your group and attempt to reach consensus. If consensus is impossible record your vote and write *your* individual response to the statement in three or more complete sentences.

1. The government should declare nicotine a dangerous narcotic and ban its production and sale. Agree or Disagree **Group Vote: Agree_____ Disagree _____**

2. Anyone can quit smoking. After all, millions of Americans have done so. Agree or Disagree. **Group Vote: Agree_____ Disagree _____**

3. The real problem in society is all the biased non smokers. Agree or Disagree. **Group Vote: Agree_____ Disagree _____**

4. Smoking is a legal product. Therefore, smokers should be able to enjoy a cigarette any place they want. Agree or Disagree. **Group Vote: Agree_____ Disagree _____**

5. The tobacco companies have lied to the American people all along. Agree or Disagree. **Group Vote: Agree_____ Disagree _____**

6. Smoking is worse than any illegal drug on the streets of America. Agree or Disagree. **Group Vote: Agree_____ Disagree_____**

7. Any pregnant woman caught smoking should have to pay a fine. Agree or Disagree. **Group Vote: Agree_____ Disagree_____**

8. The only reason people begin smoking is because they have weak self-concepts. Agree or Disagree. **Group Vote: Agree_____ Disagree_____**

9. Since it's impossible to make someone quit smoking, Jim's parents should get off his back and let him smoke until he decides to quit. Agree or Disagree. **Group Vote: Agree_____ Disagree _____**

10. The more you hang around with smokers, the more likely you are to start smoking. Agree or Disagree. **Group Vote: Agree_____ Disagree_____**

Question # 1: If you were Jim's parents, how would you handle the situation? Why? Be sure to use information and theory from your textbook to support your decision.

_____

_____

_____

_____

_____

_____

_____

_____

_____

_____

_____

_____

_____

_____

_____

_____

_____

_____

_____

_____

_____

_____

_____

_____

_____

_____

_____

_____

_____

_____

_____

Question # 2: Should tobacco be declared illegal? Why or why not? What consequences do you forsee as a result of making it illegal?

Holding Out

"The water's been turned off for a full frickin' week. Who could live like that? Animals, I tell ya! They can't shower or even flush their crappers. We turned the gas off yesterday and they should be freezing their asses off. Too bad it's only 35 degrees. It'd be nice if it got to zero, but I guess we gotta work with what we got." The little red-faced man spoke loudly and the men around him looked uncomfortable. He didn't seem to notice.

"Anyway, we should be another step closer to gettin' that trash outta there. Would ya believe it? We still got 11 apartments occupied! Shit. But we're workin' on it. Yep. We are workin' on it." Without looking at anyone in particular, he went on.

"On Wednesday, the electricity goes off. That's the last of it. Then, the cops're commin' in with riot gear on Friday to throw whatever human garbage is still stayin' in there out on the street. Monday morning, the wrecking crew arrives to level that rat hole. Animals. That's all I gotta say about it. Animals."

Anna Dean, the mayor of Ashville, was standing in the doorway staring at the man who had been speaking. Who was this guy dressed in jeans, flannel shirt, down vest, and work boots? For a second, she thought she might have gone to the wrong meeting, but the others in the large room were members of her Downtown Improvement Committee. Until now, the men—there were no women—she'd worked with in these meetings had all been dressed in suits and spoken in Ivy League English. Even the guest presenters from the builder and construction companies had looked and spoken like professionals. This guy looked straight out of some blue collar, working-class situation comedy. What had she missed by arriving a few minutes late?

"Mayor Dean!" Josh Thomas, her co-chair, appeared at her elbow and spoke loudly to announce her arrival to the group. "We didn't really start without you. Harry was just giving us a little impromptu up-date. We'll be filling you in right away, as soon as you're ready."

Silence fell as the seated men looked her way and struggled to stand as she made her way to her chair at the head of the table. Some smiled uncomfortably. She sat amidst a lot of throat clearing, rustling of papers, and audible sighs. Two low voices could be heard in whispered conversation. Studiously, she reviewed her files.

After a couple of minutes, she looked up from her notes and glanced around the room. The man in the down vest looked warm and uncomfortable. The rest of the men avoided looking at him.

"Chmnn," she gently cleared her throat and all eyes focused on the mayor. She smiled. "Good morning, gentlemen. Shall we get started? Mr. Thomas, will you go first, please? I believe you promised me an update."

"Yes. Yes, Ma'am. Ahm, first, I'd like to introduce Harry Walker, here with us today, who is the chief of security for Klein Konstruction. They asked him to be here to brief us on the progress of the Greencastle renovation project. As you know, Greencastle is on the agenda for today."

Mayor Dean, two fingers and her thumb supporting her slightly tilted head, nodded at Harry Walker. Her dark, unlined face was a mask, unreadable and as stiff as her lacquered salt-and-pepper hair. Walker was flushed and seemed angry but not quite prepared to speak. Patiently, she waited for the security chief's report.

Before Walker could speak, Josh Thomas broke in again. "Perhaps it would be best if I refreshed everyone's memory about the Greencastle project. Maybe that would put things into, ahmn, perspective."

"Go on, Mr. Thomas, a little history won't hurt any of us," the mayor agreed. Greencastle had been a thorn in her side since she'd inherited it from her predecessor. Frankly, she couldn't imagine that anyone sitting at the table was unfamiliar with every difficult aspect of its development. But maybe the telling would diffuse some of the tension certain to occur if she had to deliver the latest, and perhaps most insurmountable, demand leveled by Budding Builders.

"As you all remember," he began, "three years ago a stairwell in the A building at the Greencastle housing project collapsed. It was determined that both of the high-rise buildings were in such serious disrepair that they were unsafe. An in-depth study suggested that it was more cost effective to demolish Greencastle and rebuild it, than it was to repair it."

"It was at that time," he continued, "that our committee proposed a plan to demolish Greencastle and build residential town-homes on the four-block site, rather than high-rise apartment buildings. These units would, in part, be made available to Section-Eight public assistance recipients. The majority of the units, however, would be sold to the high-income buyers who are seeking to buy homes in the downtown area. This, we believe, will revitalize this section of downtown by providing a new flow of tax dollars, some of which will go back into additional welfare programs, while still providing some housing to the city's poor here in the downtown area."

"As it is now, Greencastle sits on prime downtown real estate and is an ugly eyesore that houses some of the city's most dangerous folks. This keeps our downtown area hostage to crime and limits potential revenue for our city. Our shopping area is depressed because shoppers are afraid to come into the city. This, of course, adversely affects our tax flow and business development that would also add to our tax dollars. Additionally, with Greencastle gone, it would give opportunity to the current residents to find better and safer housing, some of it right there in the newly created, expensive town homes set aside for some handpicked residents displaced by the demolition. With this model program, which I might add has attracted nationwide press, our hope is to help integrate Greencastle's most likely candidates for getting off welfare into a diverse community that works for everyone. Other residents are being helped to secure newer, safer dwellings at other public housing sites in and around Ashville. Everybody wins!"

Thomas took a deep breath and went on. "Naturally, as is always the case with complex issues, things didn't proceed quite as we expected. First, there was the problem of finding a builder willing to invest in a financially risky project. After all, how can we guarantee that people will want to buy expensive homes in an area with the reputation of Greencastle. We had no takers at all in the first go-around and were only able to secure the Budding Group to design and manage the project because we offered them tax incentives and," he glanced at Mayor Dean, "many difficult concessions, including the cut from ten units reserved for public housing families, to only seven. Six of which are currently spoken for, I might add."

"After two years, we believed that most of the problems had finally been solved and the project was ready to get off the ground. The biggest hurdle, the new school, had been put into the budget and redistricting was approved by the Board of Education."

"As Greencastle continued to deteriorate, many families were moved to other locations. Building A was completely empty and boarded up. The project design looked great and everything seemed to have been hammered out."

Then," he continued, "when we started relocating the folks who didn't want to move, an uproar over the destruction of Greencastle stopped the entire thing for six months while it was being reviewed by the courts. Finally, two months ago, we were granted eviction of the remaining residents. Since then, all has gone relatively well until two weeks ago when we hit a stalemate with the remaining eleven occupied apartments whose residents refused to leave unless the police became involved. They offered all kinds of reasons. They were too old, too sick, they wanted their kids to finish the term at their school, they didn't like the place they were offered, and so on. Finally, we had to act on the Order of Eviction we obtained from the courts."

He stopped and looked at Walker, "Maybe you could pick it up here, Harry."

Walker, who'd had time to compose himself, seemed ready to speak. "Ahm. Well, like I...well, let me start out by telling you who I am. See, I'm the guy who makes sure that there's no trouble on sites like this here one. You know, on some jobs, equipment gets wrecked and, well, sometimes people do stupid stuff like, well, like, last year, there was the nut who chained himself to some old tree that was in the way of us paving over a concrete slab for parking. So, well, they need a security guy like me. So, I have like six guys who answer to me who make sure there's no trouble." Walker looked pleased with this introduction and went on.

"So, when my boss at Klein Konstruction—that's the outfit that's doing the demolition of these here rat-trap apartment buildings—called me into the office and told me to set up 24-hour guards at the site, well, that's what I did. My guys was to, you know, make sure there wasn't no trouble. Also, they wanted all these people outta there. I mean, who'd wanna stay there? You gotta ask yourself...."

"Mr. Walker. Please." The mayor seemed less than her usual controlled self. It was apparent that she didn't like this inarticulate man. "What is going on at Greencastle?

What is the status of the relocation of the tenants? I'm assuming this is what you are here to report." Her smooth, slightly southern tone sounded less melodic than usual.

"Yep. I'm gettin' to that. So, that was like, two weeks ago that I posted my guys there. And I'm feelin' good about reportin' that not one incident has occurred in that time between my guys and the, ahm, tenants," he stretched out the word, "that are still there. We've been gettin' along peachy. No problems what-so-ever."

"Now, however, we are enterin' a new phase." Walker sat up importantly and continued. "In the hopes of gettin' the rest of these people outta there, we turned off the water last week just like the court order says we can, and also the gas is off and in a coupla days, the electricity goes. That hadda be saved for last due to safety reasons. Can't ask my guys to patrol in the pitch black when ya don't know what kinda animals are hangin' around."

With a smile on his face and obvious satisfaction in his tone, he finished. "Finally, the cops is goin' in on Friday to get rid of everyone else still holed up in there. And on Monday we level the both of the, ahm, buildings. Then the new homes can finally go up, and everyone lives happy ever after!"

For a few seconds, everyone around the table seemed unable to speak. They were staring at the little man not quite sure of what to make of his presentation. Finally, Mayor Dean coughed and spoke.

"Thank you, Mr. Walker. I'm sure we all appreciate your coming here today. Please feel free to stay for the rest of the meeting, if you'd like. However, if you are pressed for time, I'm sure we'd all understand if you had to leave us. Gentlemen, let's take a ten-minute break while I get an update from my office. I'm hoping to hear again from Mr. Budding about the latest Greencastle crisis I'll be reporting to you after our break. Gentlemen." Mayor Dean stood and walked briskly past the seated men.

Moving quickly through the dim hallway, looking both ways for anything that looked out of place, she let out her breath as she made it to the door. Made it. Once again, she'd come in through the hole in the fence, eluded the security guards just like her mama had taught her, and safely made it to their place. Quickly, she unzipped her coat, reached inside her shirt, and tugged on the green string that held her key. Looking around again, she inserted the key into the flimsy lock, turned the knob, stepped inside and let out another deep breath. The door banged loudly behind her. Slammed. Klareese stopped and thought about the word: slammed. How could she have made that mistake? Of course there were two m's in slammed. S-l-a-m-m-e-d. Slammed. If she had only remembered that one little m, she would have won the spelling contest six weeks in a row.

Dang! She had studied, as she always did, and had fully expected to win again. Instead, James had won. She knew that he worked hard at school, but she knew she could beat him at spelling. And English and social studies. Now math, he was better at than she was and it was really tough to out-do him on tests, but she did manage occasionally. James Washington and Klareese Brown were the best students in the fifth grade at Roosevelt Elementary. Everyone knew it. Mama and her big sister, Sharwon, were very proud.

Klareese moved across the small room and started to pull off her coat before she realized how cold it was. Quickly, she put it back on. She yanked a cup from the shelf and started across to the sink, then remembered that the water had been turned off. Instead, she poured water from a bottle her mama had filled and dragged home, into a cup and placed it into the microwave. Tea would warm her up. Might as well have some before they decided to turn off the electricity as well. She heard, in her mind, the voices of her sister and mama as she waited for the water to heat.

"School's the way out."

"School's how you git to be somebody."

"School's how you earn money to get you anythin' you want."

"You wanna be like yo' mama? Old, wi' no teeth at 35, workin' three jobs?"

"School be how you git out, 'Reese."

Klareese dunked the used teabag into the hot water and then carefully set it back onto a small plate for later use. One spoon of sugar and she was ready to go. She carried the tea over to the corner table where she and Sharwon had studied for years, and hoped for inspiration as she unpacked her schoolbooks. Sometimes, the studying got hard and she wished she could just give it up and watch TV.

But that would not happen. She could never let Sharwon and mama down. They expected more. She would be like Sharwon and she would study until she dropped if it meant getting out of Greencastle. Well, they were getting out anyway; they were being thrown out. Klareese worried that when they finally found a place, it would be a place just like this one. With dark stairs and halls and danger hanging everywhere. She just hoped she would be able to continue at Roosevelt. She couldn't bear starting over in some other school where she didn't know who the dangerous ones were. Roosevelt was no bargain, but at least she knew how to survive there. Unless she could attend a special school. One where studying was a priority and there weren't any guns and knives and you could learn without fear of getting beat up because you studied and did well on tests.

Or better yet, maybe she'd really get to go to the new school. The one being built for the rich kids who lived in the new areas of downtown and the ones who'd be living here after Greencastle was torn down. That's what her mama said would happen. That's why they were staying till the end. Her mama, who knew everyone, insisted that they'd get chosen for one of the nice, new places being built here. Mama said they were the last family that met all of the qualifications. There were seven homes for folks from Greencastle, but only six had been given away. James was staying. So were Aloyse, Marybe, Mattie and Louis, all good students. The last home, mama said, was for them. God had told her. That's why they were staying. He had promised the last one to them.

All of the men were still seated when she returned. They were speaking in soft voices, some working quietly on paperwork, others just deep in thought. Carefully, she sat and started to speak.

"I'm afraid that once again, I have to be the bearer of bad news. I'm afraid, that once again, the Greencastle project is on the chopping block and another very difficult decision must be made by this committee. I want to start by telling you that I wish to God that I had never been handed this dreadful, disastrous mess. Every time we turn around, we have another potentially impossible situation."

"And yet," she continued, "we've come so far! We've made so many concessions, but the long-term potential is great. I just can't see scrapping this entire thing. One way or another, Greencastle must be demolished. It's a hazard. Building A has been condemned and Building B is not much better."

"But I digress. Forgive me. I would just like you to keep our difficult journey in mind as I give you this latest news. Gentlemen, I was informed today by the CEO that

Budding Builders cannot make their needed profit unless we give up one more of our remaining seven units. As it is, Budding is extremely concerned about the financial repercussions of allowing public housing tenants in the project, particularly the inclusion of public housing students in the new school being built. They are prepared, gentlemen, to withdraw altogether from the project unless we cut our public housing units from seven to six." She looked at the stunned faces around the table and waited for someone to speak.

Name_____

Instructions: read each statement before coming to class. Indicate your response by circling "agree" or "disagree" at the end of the statement. In class discuss the statement with your group and attempt to reach consensus. If consensus is impossible record your vote and write *your* individual response to the statement in three or more complete sentences.

1. Providing less educational opportunities to the poor is a deliberate attempt by the affluent to maintain a privileged lifestyle for their own children. Agree or Disagree. Why? **Group Vote:** **Agree_____ Disagree _____**

2. Just because some people are able to spend more on their own kid's education doesn't mean the system is discriminatory. Agree or Disagree. Why? **Group Vote: Agree_____ Disagree _____**

3. While the poor may suffer in the short run from projects like this, in the long run the revitialization of the city will help them by creating new jobs and greater tax revenues. Agree or Disagree. Why? **Group Vote: Agree_____ Disagree _____**

4. It's not right that poor people should have to move out of their homes just to make room for the rich. Agree or Disagree. Why? **Group Vote: Agree_____ Disagree _____**

5. Mixing rich people and poor people into the same housing unit will never work. Agree or Disagree. Why? **Group Vote: Agree_____ Disagree _____**

6. It would be irresponsible for the mayor to endanger the Greencastle Rennovation Project just to save one unit for the poor. Agree or Disagree. Why? **Group Vote: Agree_____ Disagree_____**

7. Gentrification is just another word for racism. Agree or Disagree. Why? **Group Vote: Agree_____ Disagree_____**

8. Middle class families, regardless of race, will never move to the city if they have to send their children to school with ghetto kids. Agree or Disagree. Why? **Group Vote: Agree_____ Disagree_____**

9. Trying to mix kids of different socioeconomic and racial backgrounds in school to end discrimination will never work. Agree or Disagree. Why? **Group Vote: Agree_____ Disagree _____**

10. This is America, people shouldn't be forced to send their kids to school with kids from different cultural backgrounds or races. Agree or Disagree. Why? **Group Vote: Agree_____ Disagree_____**

Question #1: If you were the mayor and her council, what decisions and compromises would you make regarding the Greencastle Project? Why? Be sure to use information and theory from your textbook to support your decision.

Question # 2: Think about Klareese and her family. What is going to change their circumstances? Is it money? Education? Afirmitive Action? What? Be sure to use information and theory from your textbook to support your decision.

Laskey's Battle

Autumn had come early to Connecticut. Brought from the north, the cool Canadian air slipped down into the region in mid September and lingered like an unwelcomed guest through the early weeks of October. Unexpected, the change caught everyone by surprise, including Emily Laskey, who in a lifetime of fifty-odd seasons couldn't remember an earlier fall.

With her failing body slumped precariously in the cold metal wheelchair she stared across the courthouse lawn taking in the brilliant yellows of sugar maples and the rich, deep reds of the towering oaks. She contemplated her life against the seasons—fall to winter, life to death and then, the rebirth that came with the gentle, southern breezes of spring. How utterly poetic the seasons were, she thought. There would be no warm life-giving breezes for her. Just as sure as the increasingly bitter winds hastened the arrival of winter, the savage cancer raging in her body would wrestle life from her. Soon, she would be separated from this life and the lives of the ones she loved.

Raising a frail arm dotted with flesh-toned adhesive band-aids, she brushed away a lone tear from her cheek before regaining her composure and her resolve. Yes, if there was to be death, let it also come to the purveyors of death itself—the tobacco companies with their obscene profits extracted from the pain and torment of their victims. It was this hope, and this alone, that sustained Emily in her last earthly days. From her death would spring life for the grandchildren she would never see and the precious lives of all children to come. Let them be free of the menace that had robbed her of her life.

She felt the gentle tap of her husband on her shoulder. "It's time to go, dear," he whispered. "John says it's about to begin."

Looking up into the gentle face of the man with whom she had shared the last thirty-one years she only nodded, choosing to save her remaining strength for the battle about to begin. After three long years of legal maneuvering, with countless delays and continuances, it was about to begin—*Laskey v. Tabocco Unlimited*. Her doctors predicted she wouldn't make the verdict. The tobacco companies had counted on it. A thin smile crossed her lips. It was a personal triumph. Now, it was only a matter of a few weeks more to struggle. Then she could rest forever.

Maria Theresa Vasquez Herandez, a petite woman shy of fifty by one year, walked behind the others in short steps through the narrow hall leading to the courtroom of Judge Stephen J. Haley. As juror number seven, she would help decide what the financial and legal experts across the country were claiming to be the single largest and most important product liability suit of the century. The stakes were high, the highest, not only in terms of the potential dollars—astronomical in scope and beyond the comprehension of the ordinary citizen—but also for the life and future of an historic cornerstone of American business with billions in assets and tens of thousands of jobs for the families of this nation.

Maria Theresa could scarcely believe she was a part of the drama. A week earlier she had never even heard the term "product liability." Well, maybe she had but she certainly had not paid a moment's attention to it. Now, she and eleven others would be called upon to decide such an unclear issue. How was this possible, she silently asked herself? What did they know of such lofty and complicated matters? For heaven sakes, as she understood it, even the financial, legal, and medical experts with all their college degrees couldn't figure it out. Now, she who could barely balance her own checkbook was being asked to think in terms of millions of dollars. She still couldn't believe that she had even been selected to be a juror. After all, hadn't she been truthful when she admitted that her seventeen year-old, Jesus, God bless the stupid kid, had taken up the habit and how disappointed she was. But when asked by the defense if she could be open-minded and deliver a fair and impartial decision after hearing all the facts, she let them know, in no uncertain terms, that not once in her life had she been unfair or untruthful. As she explained, almost lecturing, that would be a very bad sin and she did her best with, of course, the help of God to always do what was right. Contemplating her plight now, she had to admit she might have overreacted to the question and that was probably what had bought her a seat on this jury. Perhaps, it was that the defense was out of preemptory challenges and their only other alternative was an openly hostile environmentalist who had lost a sister to cancer. Whatever the reason, God had chosen to give her this responsibility and she was now resolved to do His will.

Waiting for Judge Haley's arrival, Maria Theresa took measure of the overcrowded room. With virtually every seat and square foot of tile occupied, the room looked more like a country carnival than a court of law. Anxious lawyers were conferring in muffled whispers, media people were scribbling notes on small scraps of paper and the curious spectators, relegated to back rows, were straining their necks up, forward, and sideways in hopes of catching a glimpse of something, anything they could share with friends and neighbors.

The bailiff suddenly rose to his feet and admonished all to stand as he announced the arrival of Judge Haley. The judge was a tall man with thick gray hair cut short and a full beard cropped to an equal length. Calling the court to order, he quickly got down to business. There were last minute instructions for the jury, warnings to lawyers for both the plaintiff and defense, and a brief lecture on courtroom etiquette for first-time spectators. From his tone and demeanor, it was apparent that Judge Haley was a man who buckled his seat belt tightly and gripped the steering wheel firmly and with both hands. There would be little deviation in the route he had mapped out for this confrontation.

As Maria Theresa listened her eyes drifted to the plaintiff's table where the attorneys, but no Mrs. Laskey, sat. The courtroom doors opened as soon as Judge Haley finished. Amidst hushed voices and the shuffling of feet as spectators attempted to reposition themselves for a better view of the plaintiff, a dutiful and woeful husband was pushing Emily down the aisle. Stopping, the wheelchair was positioned not behind the table, but rather, to its side in full view of the jury. Her ravaged body was a ghostly and perpetual reminder to everyone of her pain and unkindly future. The defense immediately requested to approach the bench where they vehemently objected. After a furious exchange in harsh whispers, the battle was adjourned to the judge's chamber out of view and earshot of the jury.

Inside, the defense attorney, William Craine, protested vigorously over the positioning of Mrs. Laskey claiming that it was a thinly disguised ploy by the plaintiff to poison the minds of the jurors. "For God's sake," he bellowed, "why don't you just hook her up to an intravenous drip and wheel in a life support system."

John Bancroft, the plaintiff's attorney, silently nodded contemplating the idea. Ingenious, he thought. He hadn't thought of it but he was sure there was a way to work it in somewhere down the line. Perhaps if Emily's health further deteriorated and....

"Good Lord," interrupted Craine. "I was only being facetious!"

"Of course, of course," muttered Bancroft waking from his trance.

"Well, Mr. Bancroft," entered the judge, attempting to move things along.

"Your honor, our position is that Mrs. Laskey's wheelchair simply doesn't fit beneath the table and her deteriorating sight and hearing necessitate that she be positioned as close to the witness stand as possible. It is her right to see and hear what is happening in her own case." Bancroft delivered the explanation with a noticeable shoulder shrug and a seemingly sincere smile. And it was all true, especially the part about the wheelchair. However, what only he knew was that Mrs. Laskey's wheelchair was specially crafted so as not to fit beneath the table. Months prior to the trial, in the midst of all the continuances by the tobacco company, a chair had been constructed of inordinately thick aluminum tubing and oversized wheels resulting in a contraption that by its sheer size overpowered and diminished the dying woman. Hearing the plaintiff's arguments, the defense immediately offered to purchase a modified version of the chair, silver platted if necessary, that would slide comfortably under the table. With apologies for any inconvenience to the defense and the good court of Judge Haley, the plaintiff's attorney respectfully declined pointing out that as was the case with most cancer patients in the latter phases of their terminal disease, Mrs. Laskey's weakened bones had actually molded themselves to the contours of this particular chair. As a result, moving to a new chair would only exacerbate her already intolerable suffering. Surely, asserted Bancroft, his expression an amalgamation of sadness and concern, the court would not want to contribute more pain to a dying woman.

"Hell," interrupted the frustrated defense. "Just add a couple of inches to the table's legs. Then the damn thing will fit underneath."

"Now wait one minute," objected Bancroft. "You do that and we're going to look like midgets behind our table in comparison to the defense. That's an unfair psychological edge and there's a ton of research to support us on that fact."

The arguments continued for another fifteen minutes. In the end, much to the chagrin of the defense, the plaintiff's position prevailed with Judge Haley concluding that there was little recourse other than to let Mrs. Laskey remain where she was.

The first witness for the plaintiff was Dr. Henry Osterbok, a scholarly researcher late in years, and the man pictured on everyone's first home chemistry set. There was little doubt in the minds of the jurors that this man had spent most of his life in a laboratory. For over thirty years he had conducted and published research on the chemistry of tobacco. Once the defense acknowledged Dr. Osterbok's credentials, establishing him as an expert, Bancroft went to work. Through a series of charts set up in front of the jury box he proceeded to explain the complexity of cigarette smoke. To date, he stated, approximately four thousand compounds had been identified and more were being discovered each year. Of the known compounds, sixteen had been established as carcinogens, or compounds that were known to be able to induce cancer. Additionally, fourteen alkalis along with numerous other compounds had been associated with a negative biological effect on cellular structure.

Bancroft appeared genuinely stunned by Osterbok's presentation. It was as if this were the first time he had heard it. Of course, it wasn't. He and his associates had worked long hours rehearsing the researcher's testimony. He stood by the charts, looking and nodding at them in disbelief, allowing the jurors a few moments to soak up the gruesome graphics. Then he moved on. "And, Dr. Osterbok, you indicated that these compounds are native to the tobacco leaf. Are there any others we should know about?"

Osterbok leaned forward in his chair. The wrinkles on his forehead deepened, illuminating his intense concern. "Yes, in fact, I have recently published a series of articles in the *Journal of Medicine* detailing what we refer to as enhancement products."

"Is this something that someone using the product would ingest?" questioned Bancroft before letting his witness move on.

"Oh, yes," answered Osterbok immediately. "These enhancement products to which I refer were found in the cigarette smoke itself."

"And these are?"

"A number of chemicals in which the leaf is washed to enhance its flavor and manipulate nicotine levels. The primary chemical that alarms us is ammonia."

"Alarms you?" boomed Bancroft. "You mean, ammonia is harmful?"

Osterbok appeared stunned that the question was even offered. "Ammonia is a caustic compound. It's extremely destructive to human tissue. I can't imagine anyone claiming otherwise."

"Are these all the compounds you have found?"

"Yes, besides the waste products."

"Waste products?" emphasized Bancroft, turning suddenly to the jury. "And what are these, so called, waste products?" The term dripped from his mouth like acid.

"Insecticides and waste animal parts such as rodent hair and the remains of a variety of insects."

Watching some of the jurors faces contort into expressions of disgust, Bancroft knew that he had struck pay dirt on this one. "How is it possible that these waste products are found in tobacco?"

"Simply a matter of handling."

"So, what you're telling us, Dr. Osterbok, is that the tobacco industry could eliminate these so called waste products but have chosen not to."

"Objection," shouted the defense. "Dr. Osterbok is a chemist, not a manufacturer. His expertise qualifies him to testify on the chemical composition of our product, not the production process."

Bancroft conceded and restated the question. "Then perhaps you could tell us, Dr. Osterbok, what percentage of the cigarettes you have studied were polluted with these waste products?"

"We studied every cigarette on the American market."

"And?"

"Each one contained waste products."

Osterbok's testimony was so effective that it left the jury with the feeling that the cigarette was more an invention of the Pentagon than of the tobacco industry. It was exactly what Bancroft wanted them to think. Judge Haley adjourned for the day. Perfect timing for the plaintiff, thought Bancroft. It would give the jurors plenty of time to think, and perhaps even to dream, of Osterbok testimony. Certainly, they would be dark, smoky dreams.

The following morning the defense had its first crack at Osterbok. It was the collective decision of the team representing the tobacco companies to be quick and to the point, thus denying Osterbok the additional opportunity to spew out more harmful facts and figures. Craine approached Osterbok confidently. "Dr. Osterbok," he began. "You've made it your life's work to investigate the chemical composition of tobacco smoke?"

"Correct," replied Osterbok proudly.

"Could you tell us about pollution in the air we all breath."

Osterbok look surprised. "That's not my field of expertise."

"Of course, of course," he repeated. "But you do admit that there are pollutants in the air."

"Certainly."

"And would you say that these pollutants could cause cancer?"

"Some could, I suppose."

"You suppose?" countered Craine. "You mean you, as a scientist, have never read reports on air pollution and lung cancer?"

"Well, yes, I have read such reports," admitted Osterbok.

"And what was the conclusion of those studies?"

"That polluted air contributes to lung cancer."

"And isn't it true that the level of environmental pollution people are exposed to varies according to their work as well as where they live?"

"Naturally."

"Yes, indeed, Dr. Osterbok," exclaimed Craine engaging in heavy eye contact with the jury. "Perhaps," he added, "you could tell us whether the combined exposure to all of these environmental pollutants causes more or less lung cancer than tobacco smoke."

"Objection," shouted Bancroft rising. "Dr. Osterbok's expertise is chemistry, as we have established, not environmental pollution."

Craine immediately withdrew the question, confident that the issue was firmly planted in the minds of the jurors.

Again returning to the desk, he retrieved another report, this one smaller and carrying an official government seal on the front. Entering it into evidence, he handed it to Dr. Osterbok and asked him to identify it. Osterbok did so indicating that it was a series of governmental rules regulating impurities allowable in consumable products. Craine asked the doctor to turn to a certain page and read the allowable items. Osterbok read from the list, detailing a long series of chemical compounds and organic products and their allowable amounts.

"Now, Dr. Osterbok," he asked when the list was complete. "Is this not the same list of compounds and what you referred to as waste products that you described for the jury yesterday?"

Osterbok had to admit that it was true. Although they quibbled over a couple of products, there was a strong resemblance.

"Then would you not conclude that all of the food we eat contains waste products, including small traces of insecticides, dirt and the hair of rodents?"

"To some degree."

"Then how is it possible that you find the tobacco companies more culpable than General Mills who feeds tainted cereal to children?"

"I don't believe I ever...."

"That all," interrupted Craine on his way back to his table.

The second witness for the plaintiff was Dr. Hadley W. Kinsley, an African-American researcher and practicing physician specializing in oncology at the University of Chicago Hospital. Tall, handsome, and with a slight tinge of silver brushed lightly at his temples, his demeanor exuded an aura of wisdom and assuredness. Bancroft tactfully took Dr. Kinsley through the preliminaries of listing his credentials and research publications. With two medical degrees, one from Yale, the other from Boston, and a Ph.D. in statistical research methodology, he was the perfect witness for the plaintiff. By the time Kinsley finished listing his medical specialties and research publications the jurors were thoroughly convinced that if any earthly man could walk on water it had to be this one. Maria Theresa watched as one of her fellow jurors wrote Kinsley's name on the back of a business card and then tucked it carefully into his billfold. No doubt the man would later contact the good doctor on personal business.

"Dr. Kinsley," addressed Bancroft, "you have spent a number of years investigating the effects of cigarette smoke on the body, correct?"

"That is correct."

"Approximately how many years might that be?"

"In the neighborhood of twenty-five years, if you count my early graduate research."

"Nearly a quarter of a century," added Bancroft for emphasis before continuing. "Were you present during the testimony of Dr. Osterbok?"

"I was."

"Then perhaps you could offer an opinion as to its validity."

"There's no question about it. Numerous other studies have confirmed the findings of Dr. Osterbok."

"But your research differs from Dr. Osterbok's, correct?"

"That's correct."

"Perhaps you could explain to the court how it differs."

"Dr. Osterbok is a chemist. His interest and research focuses on the chemistry of tobacco smoke. On the other hand, I am a cellular biologist. My work concerns the effect tobacco smoke has on human tissue."

"So Dr. Osterbok finds the carcinogens, toxins and waste products and you investigate how they damage our bodies." Bancroft carefully enunciated the vile words as he spoke letting them sweep across the room.

"In a manner of speaking, yes."

"Please share with us how harmful these products are to our bodies." Again, Bancroft chose to include the jury in the collective "our." It was a tactic of which he was particularly fond and used often believing that the jury would increasingly identify with the plaintiff if they themselves felt violated by the product of the tobacco manufacturers. Much to his delight, the ploy seemed to be working since he and his team had noticed that only a few days into the trial two members of the jury had suddenly developed nagging coughs. By the time Kinsley was finished, he thought smiling to himself, the hacking and wheezing would spread like herpes through a seedy public bathhouse.

Dr. Kinsley rose from his chair and situated himself between the jury and a set of brightly colored charts displayed on large tripods. Withdrawing an infrared pointer from his pocket, he began to explain that tobacco smoke was actually a cloud of tiny droplets, much like the clouds in the sky. Unlike clouds that are composed of water vapor, however, the droplets of tobacco smoke contain all the harmful compounds described by Dr. Osterbok.

"When an individual smokes, he is actually inhaling a mixture of gases. About fifty percent of the smoke is retained in the lungs with a substantial amount also being deposited in the bronchial tubes." With the dot of the infrared pen racing over the charts, Dr. Kinsley carefully and in vivid language explained the effects of tobacco smoke on the respiratory system. Nearly an hour passed before Dr. Kinsley completed his depressing recitation. Then, the old charts were removed and new ones appeared containing different anatomical systems. Moving on, the doctor explained in excruciating detail how nicotine constricts the superficial vessels of the arms and legs, thus elevating blood pressure and heart pulse rate dramatically. The end result, of course, was serious deterioration of the heart muscle. The digestive system was next. He explained how the compounds in smoke mix with saliva to stimulate movement in the gut first to arouse and then to depress it. This movement, in first time smokers, produces nausea with possible vomiting. Later, the system adjusts but the damage continues. In terms of the nervous system, he continued, nicotine acts as a stimulant compounding the already serious effects to the life-supporting body organs. It was, as he put it, a multiplying factor.

"And just what is the bottom line to all of this?" inquired Bancroft.

"Death," came the answer, quick and definitive. Dr. Kinsley then proceeded to provide statistics. Three out of every ten cigarette smokers who inhale will eventually die of lung cancer. Approximately 95 percent of all cigarette smokers inhale. Over twenty years of research had demonstrated that for those individuals who smoke fifteen cigarettes a day the risk of developing lung cancer is ten times greater than for non-smokers. For those smoking two packs, the risk was twenty times greater. Increase it to three, and the risk rose to twenty-five. And this, he explained, was just lung cancer. There was still emphysema, heart disease, circulatory degeneration, dental disease, and a host of other ailments associated with tobacco smoke. "All combined, cigarettes kill 400,000 people each year."

And then, just when everyone thought that the recitation was over, Dr. Kinsley introduced the gruesome pictures—autopsies of lung cancer and emphysema victims. So graphic were the pictures that several members of the jury were forced to turn away to avoid becoming ill. Finally, the charts were removed and it was over, much to the jury's relief. Dr. Kinsley had done his job.

A dark gloom hung over the jury. Most affected was Frankie Hemp, the heaviest of the four smokers on the jury. With beads of perspiration dotting his forehead, he was perched precariously on the edge of his chair, wide eyed and chewing his fingernails. Large wet rings were growing beneath the armpits of his dark cotton shirt. The more Dr. Kinsley talked, the more frightened he became. By the time it was over, he felt downright dizzy. It was almost as if he could feel the poisons in the pack of cigarettes in his shirt pocket leaching though the cellophane wrapper into the material of his shirt where they were eating a hole right through his chest in an attempt to get at his internal organs.

It didn't take Judge Haley's years of experience to know that it was time for a break; it was written in the bluish gray complexion of the jurors. Raising his gavel, he recessed for lunch though he doubted that there would be much food consumed. Thirty minutes later, a note was passed to him in his chambers. It was an urgent request from several jurors seeking a supervised walk to the city park. Looking at the fleshy sandwich in his hand, he laid it down, put on a light jacket and proceeded to the juror's lounge.

Kinsley's testimony was devastating. Over lunch and a few cigarettes Craine debated cross-examination strategy with his team. There was little use in attacking the man's credibility—it was impeccable. Likewise, any attempt to discredit him would surely antagonize the four African-American jurors who took noticeable pride in having one of their own in such an elevated station of life. Bancroft knew this when he recruited Kinsley and they were not about to fall into his trap. For the good doctor, it would not be the sharp edge of a dagger, but rather, the sweet taste of sugar laced with arsenic.

"Dr. Kinsley," smiled Craine respectfully. "My colleagues and I were just examining some of your research," he said flipping through the pages of one of the studies. "I have to admit we were quite impressed." Again he smiled, only this time to the jurors to ensure that the four African-Americans would fully appreciate his attempt to grovel. It was a task that did not come natural to him "I noticed," he began, looking up from the pages he held, "that you concur with the work and testimony of Dr. Osterbok."

"Yes, that is true," answered Dr. Kinsley. "As I indicated, his work is well-respected in the scientific community."

"Indeed," muttered Craine, removing his glasses in a thoughtful pose. "Then you would also agree with Dr. Osterbok's admission that other pollutants such as those in the air can cause cancer."

"I believe, sir, that it was you who brought that up, not Dr. Osterbok."

"True. But Dr. Osterbok did agree, did he not?"

"Yes."

"And do you concur?"

"There is evidence to support that claim."

"Yes, there is," he stated, turning to the jury. "But for now, let's turn to your own work. I specifically refer to the autopsies you perform. I think that we all remember the pictures. For myself, I can testify that I didn't eat much at lunch." Patting his bulging stomach he joked, "hopefully, I've lost a pound or two." It was a carefully staged attempt to inject levity—the more the jurors laughed, the less anger they felt, the better for the defense. "Could you tell us the cause of death of each of the victims?" He was serious and his eyes were locked on Dr. Kinsley's.

"All of the victims were smokers."

"Yes, yes," he quickly retorted. "But can you say, beyond a doubt, that it was cigarettes that caused the cancer in each of these individuals."

Dr. Kinsley shifted uneasily in his chair. "Comparative studies between smokers and non smokers demonstrate that...."

"Excuse me, Dr. Kinsley," interrupted Craine. "We have heard that testimony before. The question is, can you prove that the cancer that the people in your autopsies had was, without question, caused by tobacco?"

"No," he stated, obviously agitated at being manipulated. "It is inferred."

"Inferred," repeated Craine, his eyebrows arching to the top of his head. "As in guess?"

"The term guess would hardly do justice to the scientific observations reached by the longitudinal studies we have conducted and analyzed."

"But still you can't, beyond all doubt, state it was the tobacco that produced the cancer."

"No, not in the context to which you have staged the question."

"Thank you, Dr. Kinsley." Craine was returning to his desk when he suddenly turned. "Dr. Kinsley," he asked offhandedly, "perhaps you could provide an answer to a question we have."

"Possibly," he replied, with the uncomfortable feeling that a trap was about to be sprung.

"Well, you see, Mr. Wilson and Mr. Hammersmidth both smoke," he said, pointing to the attorneys seated at the defense table. "Now, Mr. Wilson smokes about a half a pack day. On the other hand, Mr. Hammersmidth enjoys tobacco and smokes approximately two packs each day. You testified that there is a link between the quantity of cigarettes smoked and lung cancer, correct?"

"Correct."

"Then would it be your testimony that Mr. Hammersmidth will develop cancer before Mr. Wilson?"

"It would be impossible to make such a prediction on an individual basis."

"That's interesting," mused Craine reflectively to the jury. "Here we all are in a court of law in which millions of dollars and the livelihood of million of Americans are at stake and the best scientific mind on the subject cannot only *not* tell us who is going to get cancer first, Mr. Wilson or Mr. Hammersmidth, but he aslo can't tell us if either one will ever develop cancer. Furthermore, even if one or both of them do get cancer, he can't tell us conclusively that it's from tobacco!"

"Objection," cried Bancroft. "This is cross-examination, not summation."

"Withdrawn," retreated Craine, realizing that though the remark would be stricken from the record, it was indelibly recorded into the minds of the jurors and there was nothing Bancroft could do about it.

Dr. Kinsley was dismissed. Craine had done his job much to the relief of the smokers on the jury, particularly Frankie Hemp. The color had returned to his face, he sat upright in his chair with shoulders back and a smile on his face.

The following day the plaintiff introduced Dr. Jeffery Manning as their next witness. A research scientist, Manning had worked for Tobacco Unlimited for nearly six years before departing in a highly publicized and bitter resignation.

"And exactly what is it that you did prior to your employment at Tobacco Unlimited," asked Bancroft.

"I researched the effects of smoke condensates, usually referred to as tar, on living tissues."

"Could you tell us about your studies?"

Manning launched into describing his work. In excruciating detail he explained how he and his associates captured the tars from cigarette smoke and applied them to the skin of mice and rabbits. The end results were that those animals who had received the heaviest smears developed the most numerous and lethal tumors. Photos again were introduced much to the chagrin of the jury who had barely recovered from the last round with Kinsley. Manning then proceeded to an accounting of his work investigating the results of smoking on approximately forty short-haired dogs he taught to smoke through trachea tubes. The results conclusively proved that all of the animals suffered lung damage after a period of 850 days. The most severe damage occurred among the heavier canine smokers, those who consumed approximately eleven cigarettes per day. Manning quickly apologized for the use of dogs indicating that their sacrifice was necessary because their reaction to cigarette smoke parallels that of humans.

"Excuse me, Dr. Manning," intoned Bancroft, "this hardly seems like work that the tobacco company would be interested in."

Manning smiled: "That's exactly what I thought when they approached me. However, they explained that they were interested in developing a safe cigarette."

"You took this position?"

"Yes. I was convinced, at the time, in the sincerity of their intentions."

"And now?"

"I now know that it was a scam to get the government and the news media off their back. What they really wanted was a respected scientist with a national reputation to come to work for them just so the government and media would be satisfied with their efforts."

"And how do you know this?"

Manning eagerly explained that within two years of working with Tobacco Unlimited, he and his staff successfully produced a cigarette that substantially lowered the levels of tars and nicotine by two-thirds. His face was aglow with excitement as he described his work and the potential lives that could be saved. Then, a gloom overtook him as he began detailing the lengthy and frustrating battle he fought with Tobacco Unlimited to bring his work to the forefront and into production. At every turn, new obstacles were encountered in getting industry executives to accept his work. Finally, after two years he discovered the truth—the industry was simply not interested.

"And why wouldn't they be interested?"

"Nicotine," he replied angrily. "Nicotine sells cigarettes. It's wildly addictive and they know it. Their own studies clearly demonstrate that in times of economic hardship, smokers will forego food to buy cigarettes even to the point of malnutrition. So, the bottom line is: reduce nicotine levels and you lose customers; lose customers and you lose money. It's that's simple."

"What about the 400,000 people who die each year?" boomed Bancroft.

"They don't care about lives—they only care about money! And if there's blood on it, so be it."

"What about you? Did you resign?"

"I didn't have the chance," he stated with bitterness. "I met with the president and the chairman of the board and threatened to go public. They offered me an unbelievable salary increase, in essence a bribe, to stay and look for new cancer therapies instead of reducing tars and nicotine. I refused their blood money and was fired on the spot. I was escorted from the building by security and denied access to my notes and work. Likewise, I was informed that if I attempted to go public with my work, they would sue for violation of product confidentially."

"Did they?"

"For the last four years I've been in and out of court with them. And when that didn't work, they tried to destroy my reputation with rumors and lies. They've spent millions of dollars trying to break me."

"Have they, Dr. Manning?"

Manning hardened his gaze and turned to the defense table. "No. And they never will. Never!"

The defense pulled no punches in its cross-examination of Dr. Manning. Repeatedly they implied that he had lied both on his application form and about his intentions in accepting the job at Tobacco Unlimited. Subsequent investigations of his background revealed that his mother died after a prolonged battle with lung cancer. This, he attributed to smoking, thus blaming the industry for his mother's death. He then launched a one man vendetta against them. No, maintained the defense, Dr. Manning was not interested in research—he was interested in blind revenge. If this was not the case, then where is Dr. Manning's proof? Where is this miracle cigarette? And what of the carefully documented research records he alluded to? Their inventory of his laboratory failed to find any such records. "No," maintained Craine leaning over the railing of the jury box, "look for his motive and the motive will lead you to the truth."

The final expert presented by the plaintiff was Dr. Dorothy Sandloft, a university researcher whose specialty was market analysis and advertising. Bancroft patiently explored her credentials and work experience. Then he turned to her work with cigarette marketing. Again, the tripods were brought forward and placed in front of the jurors. Large pictures of "Joe Cool" the camel, the rugged Marlboro Man, the beautiful Virginia Slims woman, and many more were displayed. Dr. Sandloft began dissecting each ad character describing in detail the target audience. All people, she explained, have needs to fulfill and vulnerabilities. The tobacco industry has a legion of well paid psychologists whose only goal is to find new ways to exploit these needs and vulnerabilities.

"And what about the children?" inquired Bancroft.

"They are the primary target," said Sandloft without hesitation. "With four hundred thousand smokers dying each year, the industry needs new smokers to take their place. Studies clearly demonstrate that few people acquire the habit after reaching adulthood. Therefore, the next generation of smokers must come from our children—they're needy and they're vulnerable. "Think of the tobacco companies like a pack of wolves on the hunt," she said. "They never attack the strong, they seek the easy prey, the weak and helpless." Sandloft continued on for two hours. By the time she concluded, a foul mood filled the courtroom and there was little doubt of its source, the defense table.

In cross-examination, the defense's time was spent on excruciating examination of Sandloft's data. At every turn, the defense attempted to cast Sandloft's work as speculation rather than undisputed scientific fact. Others, maintained Craine, could look at the same data and come to quite the opposite conclusion as the good doctor Sandloft. This, promised Craine, would clearly be seen when the defense presented its own witnesses. After nearly two hours of sifting through data, the defense turned to Sandloft's personal life.

"Dr. Sandloft could you please tell the court at what age your father passed away?" asked Craine with his weight resting on the railing of the jury box.

"My father died at the age of fifty-four."

"And the cause of death?"

"Cancer of the esophagus."

"And did he smoke?"

"He was a pipe smoker."

Craine paused to let the fact settle into the minds of the jury. "Could it be that perhaps your conclusions are colored by your own personal biases?"

"If you are suggesting that I let my own personal loss influence my work, you are wrong. The data speaks for itself. If you're insinuating that the loss of my father was the sole motive for my work, you're wrong on that count also."

"Come now," challenged Craine. "You lost your father, a smoker, to cancer. And you are trying to tell this court that it had no influence on your work?"

"Mr. Craine," she stated firmly. "Over four hundred thousand people die of smoking related illnesses each year. It would be nearly impossible to find a scientist who hasn't lost someone to smoking."

The last witness for the plaintiff was Emily Laskey—the plaintiff herself. As predetermined in chambers, she would not be required to leave her chair to sit in the witness box. Instead, she was positioned approximately fifteen feet from, and facing, the jury. The defense would have objected, but it would have done little good other than add yet another layer to the villainous cloak in which they were already draped. Instead, they sat quietly feigning sympathetic smiles as the frail woman was wheeled into place. For his part, Craine highlighted his own smile with a slight emphatic kneading of the eyebrows. It was, he thought, the perfectly coordinated look to disguise the anger he felt. After all, how in the hell was he supposed to win this case when Bancroft was allowed to wheel his dying client all around the courtroom at every juncture of the trial? As far as he was concerned, this was nothing short of a dog-and-pony show.

The witness was in place and ready to begin. Bancroft was shuffling papers behind her. As they waited, Maria Theresa gazed upon the nearly lifeless form—a mere skeleton covered with thin, sagging tissue-paper skin. Her pale translucent eyes were hollowed deep into dark sockets and puffs of wispy white hair clung to the woman's head in a valiant struggle for life. Slowly, she turned her head until she stared directly into Maria Theresa's eyes and it was at that moment that the juror saw the face of death.

Bancroft patted his client's shoulder gingerly as he walked around the wheelchair to face her. A moment later, in short abbreviated whispers, Emily Laskey's life story began to unfold before the jury. She told of her early life with her immigrant parents and five brothers and sisters. How they had moved in search of a better life but instead had found a harsher, more intolerant one. In school, she was relentlessly tormented by her peers for her broken English and old-world dress. Desperately, she wanted to fit in, assimilate, be an American. She improved her speech, lost her accent, began dressing like her classmates. With each change came new acceptance. She was willing to do anything, sacrifice anything.

"Did that include smoking?" queried Bancroft.

"Yes, it did," she whispered. "Many girls began smoking in junior high, especially the more popular girls. It was consider cool. That's the word we used."

"And that's why you started to smoke?"

"Yes. Everywhere there were pictures of young, beautiful women with their cigarettes." She paused to breathe. "They all looked so perfect, so happy, so alive. We had no idea what we were doing."

"Did you ever think to quit?"

"Yes. In fact, I thought to myself...." She paused, coughing slightly, and Bancroft offered water. Taking a sip, she began again. "When I started, I thought that it would be for just a little while. I would quit soon. But I didn't understand how addictive it was. In a matter of only a few weeks my body screamed for cigarettes." The woman hung her head as she continued to tell the jurors of her journey through life as a smoker. She told how the craving for nicotine grew until she was smoking three packs a week.

She described in vivid detail how cigarettes dominated every aspect of her life, every moment carefully scripted until the next cigarette and the relief it brought. Likewise, she told of her battle to quit, the endless professionals, the endless gimmicks, the thousands of dollars wasted by her family in a desperate attempt to end the nightmare. And then the cancer came. Tears filled her eyes as she told of her shame and the guilt for the pain and suffering she had caused her loved ones.

"And could you tell us how it was that you came to file suit against Tobacco Unlimited?" It was more of a request than a question.

"It was five years ago, almost to the day. Half of my right lung had been cut away. Then cancer was discovered in my left lung. I was fifty-one years of age. My hope was gone. I knew I would die in the very near future. I was ashamed, depressed. I was sitting in my hospital room," she coughed and then continued, "trying to decide if God would punish me if I ended it all. I wanted so desperately to die. My poor husband, my kids...." tears welled up in her eyes again. She wiped them dry before continuing. "I remember the day so well. The TV was on in my room, the news. I don't know why or how I heard, maybe God, you know? But there they were, the tobacco men in their expensive suits speaking before Congress. I listened to them. They said tobacco was not addictive, that there was no evidence that smoking caused cancer. They were saying these things and I was dying. Even then, my body wanted cigarettes. How could they lie like that? The more I listened, the angrier I became."

"And that's when you decided to take action?"

"Yes," she said, her voice rising. "All the years I had blamed myself—totally, completely." Again, her testimony was interrupted by coughing. "But it was then that I realized the truth. You can sell anything to desperate kids, if you know what to promise them. These people," she said, turning to the defense table with obvious pain to point, "they know. And they have millions of dollars to push them." Turning back to the jury, she asked, "Can we blame our children?" She stopped momentarily, as much to rest as to collect her thoughts. "That's the reason I contacted Mr. Bancroft. My time is over. I can't undo what's been done to me. But I can help others. So can you."

The following day, it was the defense's turn. Craine approached Emily Laskey and expressed his heartfelt sympathy for her pain and suffering even though he made it clear that they disagreed on the cause of her illness. "Mrs. Laskey," he asked, "your husband smoked, did he not?"

"Yes."

"For how long?"

"Ten years."

"And, yet, after years of smoking he was able to quit."

There was no response from the woman until he asked a second time.

"Yes," she admitted.

"And do you know of others who have quit?"

"Yes."

"Many?"

"Some. But I also know many who can't quit."

Craine nodded. He was not willing to argue with the woman. Just his luck she would break into a round of coughing and die on him. No, his approach would be more subtle.

"Mrs. Laskey, you live in a metropolitan area, do you not?"

"Yes."

"Is there much air pollution?"

"I'm not sure."

"Well," he paused reflectively, "has an air pollution watch even been announced around the area where you live? You know, like the ones where they warn the elderly and people with respiratory illnesses to stay at home."

"Yes. But not often."

"But they do have air pollution." Craine did not expect an answer. Flipping a page in the report he held in his hand, he asked, "I see here that your father died of heart failure."

"Yes."

"And what was the cause of his heart failure?"

"Cholesterol. Blocked arteries."

Craine nodded knowingly. "And did you ever considering suing producers whose products contained unusually high quantities of fat?"

"Of course not. That's absurd," she coughed.

Again Craine backed away from argument. He flipped several pages before stopping. Hesitating, he thumped the report with his pen as if he were silently debating with himself. He sighed heavily. "Mrs. Laskey, it's not our intention to cause you any more suffering but there is one item we need to cover for the jury, you understand." Removing his glasses he rubbed his eyes with the thumb and index finger of one hand. If he played the part of a reluctant defense attorney, he did it well. "I see that you and your husband lost a young son."

Emily stiffened at the mention of the tragedy.

"Could you tell us the circumstances surrounding his death?"

"Objection," protested Bancroft springing to his feet.

"On what grounds?" shouted Craine back to Bancroft.

"Immaterial and antagonizing the witness."

"Ridiculous," defended Craine. "The plaintiff has taken wide latitude in speculating about cause. Do we not have similar rights or this a one-way street?"

"Objection overruled," Judge Haley said reluctantly.

"I ask again," requested Craine, softening his voice, "what was the circumstance surrounding your son's death."

"Gunshot," she replied weakly. "He was playing with his father's pistol."

"And did you bring suit against the gun manufacturers?"

"No."

"That's all. Thank you Mrs. Laskey."

The following week the defense began its case. Brevity and conciseness would dominate their strategy for several reasons. First, and foremost, Mrs. Laskey's health was failing rapidly. Her death would undoubtedly provoke powerful sympathy for the plaintiff's case. Secondly, Bancroft's skill at cross-examination was well known and they did not want to provide him a cross for their own crucifixion. And lastly, the jury was beginning to shows signs of weariness. They had driven home many of their own positions during cross-examination of plaintiff witnesses; it was now time to wrap it up.

The "wrap-up" as Craine dubbed it to his own team, consisted of a series of witnesses that would first establish that there was no conclusive scientific evidence proving beyond doubt that cigarettes caused lung cancer. Likewise, there was no clear scientific evidence supporting the addictive claims presented by the plaintiff. If it was addictive, it was no more so than perhaps chocolate, alcohol, fatty foods, etc. And finally, a professor from a prestigious university testified that her own research failed to demonstrate the claims by the plaintiff that children are the targets of the industry.

Much to the relief of the jury, after four weeks of grueling testimony and cross-examination, it ended when the defense rested. Closing arguments were set for Monday and members of the jury were excused for the weekend after a reminder of their obligations.

The closing arguments proved to be a masterpiece of rhetoric and showmanship with both attorneys demonstrating a keen and highly sharpened intellect cultivated by years of experience. The defense was first. In simple and logical language, Craine anchored his defense on two major points. First, Tobacco Unlimited produced a legal product for adults. If used properly, with restraint, it posed little harm to its user. Certainly, if abused it might be harmful. But how was that any different from any other product on the market today? "Guns, butter, chocolate, cars, alcohol," cried Craine, "they all can kill if used improperly. Should we sue their manufacturers? What would become of America if suddenly the flood-gates were opened for people to sue anyone and everyone? It would be utter chaos. The financial institutions of America would collapse." Craine walked briskly to the railing of the jury box where he made his second point. "Of course," he intoned, "this presupposes that Mrs. Laskey's cancer was caused by smoking. How do we know this is true? Even the plaintiff's own witnesses acknowledged that many carcinogenic substances exist in our environment. No one can conclusively prove that Mrs. Laskey's cancer was, without question, caused by smoking. If so, how is it possible to blame Tobacco Unlimited?" For well over an hour Craine sought to undermine the plaintiff's case as speculative and scientifically unsound.

Finally, he sought closure. "Ladies and gentlemen," he said with a knowing nod of his head. "Something's gone terribly wrong in America. Somewhere along the way we took a wrong turn. Suddenly, we have become a dangerously litigious society. A cup of hot coffee spills and a million-dollar suit is filed. Tap the bumper of the car in front of you and you're sued for thousands of dollars. Try to protect your home and the burglar is awarded tens of thousands of your hard-earned dollars. Is this our future? A society where no one takes responsibility for his or her own acts—a society where people are encouraged to seek financial gain from the most inconsequential act." Tapping the jury box railing, Craine pronounced earnestly, "I suggest to you that this country is at a historical crossroads. Our country's future is in your hands. Decide for the plaintiff and you'll paralyze the progress of this nation with an endless array of frivolous lawsuits. Decide for the defense and you'll reaffirm a value so powerful and so American that without it our future is doomed. That value is simply taking responsibility for one's own actions."

It was Bancroft's turn. Beginning, he quickly summarized the mountain of scientific evidence pointing to tobacco as the culprit in 400,000 deaths per year. How could they dispute the facts and testimony of the leading scientists of the day? How could they deny what every human being who ever smoked could tell them—smoking is addictive; quitting is torturous at best, impossible at worst. Certainly, many have quit, but that does not mean everyone is capable of quitting, nor does it mean that smokers will not develop cancer before they quit or shortly thereafter. Likewise, the evidence clearly established that Tobacco Unlimited was well aware of the dangers of smoking. And even with this knowledge, not only did they continue to produce their deadly products, but actually attempted to increase nicotine levels so as to increase sales. Why else did they reject a safer cigarette when it was in their power to produce one? "Money!" boomed Bancroft. "Without our children, they can't survive. And what if, as the statistics clearly demonstrate, one out of every three of those children eventually dies from using their product? Do they care? No, they do not care. They care only about profits and dividends and stock options. The lives of our children pale when compared to their enormous greed."

Bancroft wiped the sweat from his brow. Looking to Emily Laskey, he pleaded for the woman. "Mrs. Laskey was a child once. It's easy for us to overlook that now as we see her seated in this courtroom." Bancroft paused to walk to the jury rail. "And like the millions of our children who will be seduced into smoking this year, she too was vulnerable. Can we fault her for that? I think not. What we can do is fault those that preyed upon her vulnerability—those who prey upon the vulnerabilities of all our children." Again he paused. "I suspect in the last four weeks you have asked yourself more than once why this enormous burden has been placed upon your shoulders. Let me tell you why. It is because you are the only ones that can help us to re-think how we see tobacco. As incredulous as it seems, it is true. Do not look for the government and all their experts to solve the tobacco problem. The truth is that they have been bought. Yes," he screamed with hands flailing above his head, "bought by the tobacco companies and their hundreds of millions of dollars in campaign contribution. Why else does the government use your hard earned dollars and give subsidies to tobacco growers? Why else, when hundreds of thousands of Americans fall deathly ill to cancer, heart disease, emphysema and all the other tobacco related sicknesses, does the government again come to you and demand more money to pay for the treatment of dying smokers? Why don't they take the money from those that caused the sickness—the tobacco companies? Because," he whispered dramatically, "they have been bought. That's why we have to solve the problem, because the government won't. It's up to you."

Bancroft paused to wipe his brow again. He turned to his client. His voice, barely audible, was soft, pleading. "Mrs. Laskey will not see the glory of another spring. Mrs. Laskey will not see her grandchildren grow-up or the faces of those not yet born. Mrs. Laskey's daughters will no longer be able to call their mother to seek her wisdom or share with her the joyous moments of raising their own children. Mr. Laskey will no longer be able to seek the comfort of his wife's arms in times of trouble and uncertainty. For Mrs. Laskey and her loved ones, these precious moments are over. There is nothing we can do for them. But," he said, sweeping his arms open as if gesturing beyond the courtroom, "you can save our children."

Laskey's Battle　　　　　　　　　　　Name_____

Instructions: read each statement before coming to class. Indicate your response by circling "agree" or "disagree" at the end of the statement. In class, discuss the statement with your group and attempt to reach consensus. If consensus is impossible record your vote and write *your* individual response to the statement in three or more complete sentences.

1.　Emily Laskey knew the risks involved with smoking and refused to quit. She has no one to blame but herself. Agree or Disagree. **Group Vote: Agree_____ Disagree _____**

2.　The real villains in this story are the politicians who have been bought off with campaign money from the tobacco industry. Agree or Disagree. **Group Vote: Agree_____ Disagree _____**

3.　The only solution for the nation is to ban tobacco immediately. Agree or Disagree. **Group Vote: Agree_____ Disagree _____**

4.　Smokers should not be allowed to smoke in indoor facilities where non smokers are present. Agree or Disagree. **Group Vote: Agree_____ Disagree _____**

5.　You can't blame tobacco executives. They are only trying to make a profit from a legal product. Isn't that what capitalism is all about? Agree or Disagree. **Group Vote: Agree_____ Disagree _____**

6. If you ban tobacco, people will just find another vice to replace it. Agree or Disagree. **Group Vote: Agree_____ Disagree_____**

7. If people are able to sue the tobacco companies for cancer, then the automobile industry should be sued for the pollution emitted from car exhaust. Agree or Disagree. **Group Vote: Agree_____ Disagree_____**

8. There is simply too much government regulation in our lives. Agree or Disagree. **Group Vote: Agree_____ Disagree_____**

9. Even with all the information available about the harmful effects of tobacco, most adolescents are incapable of making a rational decision about smoking. Agree or Disagree. **Group Vote: Agree_____ Disagree _____**

10. Since tens of millions of people have quit smoking, it can't be that difficult. Agree or Disagree. **Group Vote: Agree_____ Disagree_____**

Question # 1: If you were a juror in this case, would you vote for or against the tobacco industry? Why?

_____

_____

_____

_____

_____

_____

_____

_____

_____

_____

_____

_____

_____

_____

_____

_____

_____

_____

_____

_____

_____

_____

_____

_____

_____

_____

_____

_____

Question # 2: Do you think that we should ban the production and sale of tobacco? Why or why not? What consequences might there be if a ban on tobacco was implemented?

New Dawn

Sweat and salt seeped through every pore of his body as he raced frantically through the narrow, steamy basement corridors. Up one passageway and down another, he searched desperately for the door that would lead him to Danielle's nightmare. He had to succeed, he thought, as he pushed himself harder. He was mankind's last hope—there was no room for failure. Arriving at a new set of hallways he paused momentarily wondering which corridor to enter. He wiped the sweat from his eyes and peered down the length of each but only the dim fluorescent light filled the space. His chest heaved uncontrollably and his heart beat with a force so strong that he thought it would surely burst. For the first time, he felt the exhaustion that permeated every muscle of his body. Falling against the wall, he slid to a crouch and buried his head in his hands. It seemed hopeless. Then, from the far end of the hall facing him, there was laughter. Danielle's laughter, the sound was unmistakable. The sadistic crackle reverberated through the empty space in a deafening and inhuman pitch. He rose slowly. For the first time, panic seized him and he wanted to retreat to the service elevator that had carried him down to this unearthly hell. If he stayed, he might never breathe the air above, sweet with natural fragrances, or feel the warm sunshine on his face. God, how he enjoyed feeling the warm sun, or a gentle breeze playing with his hair. No, it was too much to ask he concluded, no one should be asked to sacrifice so much. Life was far too precious to squander the last moments of existence here in this ghastly place. He turned quickly and began his retreat. Then, he stopped once again. No, he couldn't. What about the world? What was to become of its children? What about his own child? He pounded the wall cursing his fate. Danielle's laughter grew louder, drowning out his every thought. Summoning up all the courage he could, he resolved himself to face her. Slowly, he moved forward, sheltering his body against one wall of the passageway. To his surprise, the wall curved to the left. Now, he understood why Danielle was shielded from his vision. He was close and even though he could not see her or she him, intuitively he was certain that Danielle was aware of his presence.

Again the wall curved, this time to the right, and he quickly changed sides. A few more steps and he would be there. He sensed it and it was soon to prove true. As he slid cautiously around the final bend, he caught sight of her standing in front of pair of stainless steel doors ending the passageway. She wore a wicked, confident smile and her eyes never left his. He edged closer.

"Stop, imbecile," she commanded. "You're allowed no closer."

"Forget it, Danielle," he responded. "You stop. You can't go through with this; you have no right."

"Right!" She laughed again. "Who bestows the gift of right—you? The government? Or, perhaps, the church?"

"It's not natural."

"You're wrong. That which is, is natural. That is the law of the universe. And Orien lives. See for yourself," offered Danielle as she pressed what he took to be a hydraulic release. Parting at the center, the doors slid slowly open. He strained to see within, but his view was clouded by a cool, purplish mist escaping from the opening. It had a foul, almost putrid, odor.

"No! Close it before it's too late," he pleaded.

"It is too late," she shrieked. "No one, not even you, can stop what's been set in motion. It is destined to be!"

"No!"

Danielle paid no attention to his plea. Instead, she began waving her arms wildly above her head while invoking a strange incantation. Over and over, she chanted as if attempting to call upon some demonic spirit. As the mist slowly evaporated he stood helplessly by, mesmerized by a fearful sense of anticipation. All events seemed beyond his control now. Danielle, who had ceased her chanting, was smiling proudly as it appeared. Stepping out from the curtain of mist it revealed itself in full form. Disbelief seized him as he gazed upon its enormous body. Standing nearly seven feet tall it was perfect in every aspect—large straight shoulders, muscles crisscrossing the torso and extremities in magnificent testimony to strength, rich newborn-blue eyes, and with features smooth and polished. Only its skin deviated from perfection. It resembled a thin sheet of rubberized plastic stretched taut across the entirety of the creatures form. Its effect was surrealistic and unnatural.

The mist had cleared, but the stench remained. The creature stood facing Danielle in absolute obedience. She, in turn, gazed back with loving eyes. It was as if the two were welded together in a bond of mutual commitment.

"Give it up, Danielle," he commanded. "It violates natural law. You're destined to lose. Get rid of it! Now!"

"Never," replied Danielle indignantly. "Orien is perfect—he is forever."

For the first time, he smiled because he knew that on this point he possessed power over Danielle. "Only for a short time. Have you forgotten the embryos? I have them in my lab—in my freezer. I'm first in command—you're second. It's my decision that controls Orien's destiny and the embryos, not yours."

An expression of horror crossed Danielle's face as she listened to his words. Clutching the creatures arm tightly with both hands, she whispered her message.

In a low agonizing moan the creature uttered, "live." The word was unmistakably clear and hung in the thin air. "Live," it again moaned. Watching Danielle, he saw her bark her message as she swung her arm forward and pointed directly at him.

He moved backwards and shouted, "No! Don't do this!"

The creature turned to face him. Its face was expressionless—the commitment to his destruction unquestionable. Pivoting, the man raced to the elevator but in a matter of seconds it was on him. The creature's immense arm sent him sliding across the polished floor and crashing up against a wall. Pain racked his body but no bones seemed broken. The creature reached down and grabbed him by the shirt, raised him well above the floor, and for a brief second stared into his eyes. Then, it emitted a groan and hurled his body up into the air and against the opposite wall. From inside his body he heard the sound of bone breaking and simultaneously pain stabbed at his left shoulder. Broken, he thought, as desperation seized him. Unless he could do something quickly, the next blow would end it. He saw Orien looking at Danielle who was standing at the end of hallway. It seemed reluctant to deal the final blow but he was sure that it would come. Above him, he saw the faucets of the overhead sprinkler system and across the hall, less than ten feet away, was the emergency release system. His mind raced, searching for some sort of advantage that would allow him to escape.

Then it occurred to him. The creature's skin, unlike his own, was smooth, nonporous, and lacking in traction. If he could lay down a thin film of water over the surface of the already slick floor it might, just might, give him the edge that he needed. But could he do it? His body was bruised and broken; would it respond to his command? It was now or die. Closing his eyes, he focused all of his mental energy into catapulting to the opposite side of the hall. In one swift blow he shattered the glass encasing the emergency release level. Pain shot through his hand as the jagged glass cut deeply into the *soft tissue of his palm. Grabbing the lever, he pulled and immediately the sprinklers responded with a flood of water. The creature was startled. It stood looking up at the water spraying from the faucets and wiping its eyes with long sweeps of its arms. Struggling to his feet, he staggered toward the elevator. In the background, he could hear Danielle screaming at Orien who was still preoccupied by the spray of the water over him. The word "live" from Danielle finally broke Orien's spell and once again he became the object of the creature's attention. From behind him, he could hear Orien bellowing angrily. But as it lumbered forward in chase, the creature slipped and crashed to the floor. Its legs struggled for balance, but the loss of traction made even the slightest motion difficult. He sped toward the elevator knowing that in moments Orien would learn to negotiate the slick surface. Ahead, he could see the opened doors of the elevator. Behind, he could hear Orien's struggling footsteps. Reaching the elevator, he hurled himself into it and quickly pushed the up button. Nothing...*

BANG! The door slammed hard against its frame startling Phillip Wells who had fallen asleep at the desk. Through hazy eyes he saw Dr. Danielle Parker standing in front of him. Dressed in a long, white lab coat she stood glaring at him.

"Who let you in?" she demanded to know.

"Night security," he responded groggily, rubbing his eyes.

"Impossible," she countered. "They have no authority to admit anyone to this office."

"Yes, so I was informed."

"Then how?" she again demanded.

Wells was fully awake now. "I simply convinced them that they had misinterpreted security directives. That I, as Chief Medical Researcher for the Institute had clearance for all offices—no exceptions. Otherwise, how else could I fulfill my obligations? It took some talking, but eventually they fell victim to my administrative mumbo jumbo." Wells paused momentarily, then, looking up, he remarked, "It's frightening...you know, the power of language."

"I don't give a damn about your persuasive powers. What are you doing in my office?"

"There's a big hole in the Institute that keeps sucking up tens of thousands of research dollars. I figured that it was my job to locate that hole and find out what's at the bottom of it."

"That's none of your business," Danielle shot back. "The money does not belong to the Institute. It comes from a private benefactor and…"

"Yes," interrupted Wells, "I know all about your special benefactor, Danielle."

"You do?" For the first time Danielle appeared genuinely puzzled. "How could you know?"

"Easy," responded Wells, smugly picking up a file folder on the desk before him and holding it up for her to see, "I read the latest progress report to your benefactor—the military."

Danielle's eyes widened in disbelief. She raced to the file cabinet and opened the drawer marked CONFIDENTIAL in bold letters. "It's been opened!" she cried.

"Yeah, I know," replied Wells holding up a Swiss Army pocketknife with a small thin blade. "A little trick my father taught me. Did I ever mention that he was a locksmith?"

In three quick steps, Danielle reached her desk and snatched the report from him. Racing back to the file cabinet, she pushed the folder back into the top drawer and hurriedly closed it. "You're in big trouble, Wells," she hissed in a voice dripping with venom. "I'm going to have you arrested for this."

Wells laughed. "C'mon Danielle, who do you think you're talking to, some administrative imbecile? I'm a scientist. I can read a medical file. I know exactly what you and your fascist friends are up to here, and the last thing you want is a police investigation." Wells stood. Leaning over the desk while supporting his weight with his hands, he continued, "then, everyone would know, wouldn't they? They'd find out about these hideously inhuman experiments of yours. I doubt you'd want that to happen."

"Get out!" shouted Danielle. "Get out!"

"I'll leave," replied Wells as he walked slowly to the door. "But don't think this matter is finished."

"Oh, yes," smiled Danielle. "You have no idea how right you are Dr. Wells. This matter is far from finished."

Wells paused before leaving. Danielle's eyes were ablaze with anger. Turning, he left the office and made his way down the corridor to the elevator. Inside, he pushed the top button and waited to be carried to his sixteenth floor office. As the elevator rose, he contemplated Danielle's words. What did she mean by that last remark? Her tone had conveyed an air of conspiracy. To what lengths would she and her supporters go to maintain secrecy? Surely, they wouldn't...no, laughed Wells. Even Danielle wasn't capable of such treachery.

Back in his office, Wells paced the floor in anxious anticipation of the arrival of Dr. Wesley Cannon, the Institute's Chief Executive Officer, en route from Washington, D.C. Suddenly, slumping into his chair, he checked his watch. It would be five hours before he could see Cannon and inform him of Danielle's experiments. Dr. Cannon had served as the Institute's CEO for fifteen years. He was a man of impeccable moral character and committed to the sanctity of human life. If anyone could handle this, thought Wells, it would be Cannon. But he'd need information, the latest information. He had to be prepared for the meeting. Picking up the phone, he called home.

"Hello," answered his wife, Cathy.

"It's me, honey."

"What's going on, Phil? I got this strange call from your secretary telling me that you wouldn't be coming home last night. Something about a research project needing your attention."

"It's a little more complicated than that, Cathy."

"What's up?"

"Nothing I can talk about on the phone." There was a pause on the other end of the line. "Listen, I need you to call Ernie and tell him to meet me for lunch, say around noon, at that restaurant we usually go to when I'm downtown. He'll know which one."

"Ernie? Why do you need to talk with Ernie? He's a...."

"Cathy," he interrupted. "I just have some time and I'm going to be downtown. Besides, I owe Ernie lunch, he treated me the last time. By the way, use his private number. It's listed in the back of my schedule book, got it?"

"Wait a minute," she said, fumbling through the desk. "Here it is," Wells heard pages flipping. "It's..."

"Yeah," he interrupted again. "That's it. Just call and tell him I'll be there around noon."

It became apparent to Cathy that she was not to mention anything about Ernie on the phone, not his occupation or telephone number. "But what if he can't make it?"

"Ernie?" he laughed. "Do you really think Ernie would turn down a free lunch? Just call, he'll be there."

"Is everything all right?" she asked with a slight waver in her voice.

"Sure," he replied, reassuringly. "There's really nothing to be concerned about. We'll talk when I get home tonight." The two exchanged good-byes and hung-up. Buzzing his secretary, he made arrangements for a cab to pick him up. Minutes later, he was standing outside the Institute, waiting. The brisk autumn air felt good to Wells. When the cab arrived, he slipped inside and gave the driver instructions.

"Hey, Mack," called the cab driver as he studied Wells in his rear-view mirror. "You look beat, really beat, know what I mean?"

"Yeah," he muttered.

"Take a nap. It's gonna be at least forty-five minutes."

"I wish I could, but I can't."

"Hey, if it's the driving, don't worry. I've got a perfect record, no wrecks. Besides," laughed the cabby, "if we do have a wreck, you're better off asleep anyway. It'd be less painful." He laughed harder this time, amused at his own humor.

Wells smiled, too weak to think. If only he could close his eyes and sleep. What he wouldn't give for some sleep. He was tired...so tired. Laying his head back, he closed his eyes for just a moment of rest...just a moment...

Slamming his fist against the button again, Wells nearly broke the bones in his fingers. "C'mon, c'mon," he shouted. Looking up he could see Orien approaching in short, hurried steps that, considering the slick footing, were remarkably effective. It would be only a matter of minutes before the creature reached the elevator. And with Orien blocking the corridor leading to the stairs, the elevator was his only hope. Again he pounded the button but the doors remained frozen. It was hopeless. Don't panic, remain calm, think, he coached himself. Then, a thought occurred to him—a long shot. An electronic relay switch wired to the door triggered the power unit that controlled the elevator's lift and descent. Evidently, the switch had become wet with the water pouring through the basement and wouldn't activate. His only hope was to bypass the relay switch and activate the main power unit directly. Quickly, he reached into his pocket and pulled out the Swiss Army knife given to him as a boy by his father. His broken shoulder made opening the knife's thick steel blade difficult and he winced with pain. Then, he went to work on the panel without looking up. He knew that Orien was closing the distance. The unit was new and the upper screws holding the front plate came away easily. Not bothering with the bottom, he reached up and bent the plate down revealing complex wiring. Quickly, he scanned the wiring chart imprinted to the left of the unit and located the relay switch. Next, he found the wire connected to the sixteenth floor switch and ripping both from the circuit, he held one in his right hand and attempted to grasp the other with his left. The hand would not respond. Bending over, he grabbed the wire with his teeth holding its bare end firmly in his mouth. From the corner of his eye, he caught a glimpse of Orien—the creature was nearly upon him. Only one course of action was open to him now. Knowing that his saliva would provide the necessary bridge to establish a flow of current between the two wires, he closed his eyes tightly, knowing what would come, and stuck the other wire into his mouth. Immediately, the current sparked across his mouth in a loud crack and sent him sprawling. He lay crumpled in a corner and shook his head in an attempt to clear his vision as the elevator slowly began to rise. Jubilation overcame him and he stamped his feet in a display of joy as less than ten feet away Orien was approaching quickly in short, determined steps. The elevator with it's unusually large opening was rising slowly—too slowly. Orien closed the gap between them and then, at the last instant, flung its body at the rising platform. Catching it chest high, the creature managed to secure a firm grip that would allow it to lift itself up and into the elevator. Grabbing his shoulder to brace his broken collarbone, Wells scooted across the floor of the elevator and arriving at just about the time Orien's face appeared, he reared back and with a forceful thrust of his foot landed a kick squarely on Orien's jaw.

The creature's head snapped back and it lost the grip of one hand. With the other hand, it clung to the rising platform while its body dangled, unaware that the elevator's opening was narrowing rapidly as the platform and the upper ceiling beam approached each other. Wells' first impulse was to deliver another blow to the fingers of the one hand still clutching the elevator's floor, but a quick assessment of the situation made him realize that Orien was unaware of the impending disaster awaiting him. Wells' heart raced faster and faster as he waited for the moment to arrive. No longer was he thinking about the pain stabbing at his shoulder. "Yeah!" he shouted in victorious celebration as the opening closed, trapping the creature's fingers. The elevator began to jerk violently in an effort to shear away the fingers obstructing its upward lift. From below, he could hear Orien's agonizing screams while above him the electrical motor screeched and sparked. The noise of creature and machine struggling against one another was almost unbearable. Wells sat helplessly awaiting the outcome. For a brief moment it appeared that the creature would outlast the machine. But then, when the tissue surrounding the fingers compressed and blood began to spill onto the elevator floor, Wells knew that the victory was his. An instant later, he heard the sound of crushing bone and slowly the fingers turned upward and were pinched, one by one, from the hand. The elevator shut-

tered and then moved upward. His head fell backward into the corner and he nearly passed out. From half-open eyes, he watched the numbered lights as they raced up the elevator board. "Welcome to the real world, you son-of-a-bitch," he muttered.

Phillip Wells jumped, hitting his head against the roof of the cab. The door to the cab was open and the driver was shaking his shoulder trying to rouse him to a state of consciousness. Blinking his eyes, Wells attempted to focus on the face in front of him.

"Hey, Mack," said the cab driver, " that was one heck of a dream you were having. Monsters, eggs, demons, what not. What kinda work you in anyway?"

Phillip shook his head. "Nothing exciting. Must be watching too much television, huh?"

"Whatever," remarked the cab driver. "Be twenty dollars and forty-five cents."

Phillip handed the man twenty-five and slipped quickly into the restaurant. He found Ernie Kosovich at a booth in the back. Ernie was a close friend who had been an investigative reporter on the Daily Times for the last twenty years.

Kosovich watched his friend slide into the booth opposite him. "From the looks of you, either Cathy's leaving you, you got yourself fired, or you're dying."

"That bad, huh?"

"That bad."

Phillip leaned over the table. He kept his voice low. "Ernie, for now this has got to be off the record. You agree?"

The newspaper man nodded.

"Do you have anything on any secret government project called the Del-Phi?"

"Can't say that I have. What's it all about?" he inquired.

"Something to do with embryonic research and DNA restructuring."

The man's eyebrow shot up, etching deep crevices into his forehead. "Like the creation of mutant lifeforms?"

"Something like that."

"Jesus," he whispered. "Sure, there have been rumors. But nobody is taking it seriously. I mean, there's no evidence, right?"

Wells sat quietly staring back at the newsman.

"Good, God," he exclaimed, "it's true. The military is trying to create mutants. You've gotta let me in on this, Phillip. This is an important story. These military people can be dangerous. The American public needs some warning."

Phillip held up his hand. "Not yet. I'm still trying to handle it internally. I don't really know everything. I have my suspicions and I'm working to get to the bottom of it."

"But you will let me know?"

"Only if I can't handle it internally."

"But the public..."

"Listen," responded Wells, "we're doing some pretty important research at the institute that will eventually benefit a lot of people. Exposing Del-Phi will shut down all our research. I can't let that happen. At least not if I can handle it internally."

"And if you can't?"

"That's why you're here."

Phillip Wells returned to his office. He slumped into his chair behind his desk and looked at the clock on the wall. It would be one half hour before he would be able see Dr. Cannon. He laid his head on the desk and closed his eyes.

An eternity seemed to pass before the elevator slowly ground to a halt. Looking up, Wells could see that he had reached his destination. He pulled himself off the floor and rested the weigh of his body in the corner while regaining his composure. Nothing could stand in the way of his mission, he thought, not the pain, not the exhaustion, not Danielle, and especially, not her hideous creation, Orien. Using the elevator wall for balance, he slid his body forward to the control panel and pushed the hold button. If Orien was going to get him, he would have to come up the nineteen flights of stairs on foot. Stumbling from the elevator, he looked down the hall to the exit door. It had to be locked. He straightened his body and took the first few steps before stopping to rest. Though a bit wobbly, he was surprised at the strength remaining in his battered body. Smiling, he now knew that victory would be his. He took a few more steps and broke into an unsteady lope.

The stairway door was a good one, double reinforced metal without a window. In normal day-to-day use it opened from either side. To engage the locking mechanism the long tubular handle on his side had to be raised and then locked with a key that he did not possess. Once locked into place, the door could only be opened from his side. How could he secure the handle in an upright position? Across the hallway he spied a cleaning cart. If slid underneath the handle, it might be just the right height to force the locking mechanism into place. Racing to the cart, he quickly rolled it to the door and raised the handle, forcing it into place. Finally, to insure that the cart could not be jolted loose he took a long towel, and using his knife cut it lengthwise reducing its bulk. He then tied the cart into place and yanked hard several times to test the knot. It was secure. He now felt safe to turn his attention to his mission—the embryos.

His laboratory was less than a hundred feet away. Quickly, he made his way toward it, more confident than ever that he would be able to complete his mission. How incredible that this important moment in human civilization would never be recorded in history. Even in success there would be the need to maintain secrecy, to prevent other insane scientists with unholy ambitions from knowing about Danielle's success. Otherwise, they would be encouraged to dabble in human creation experiments. Reaching the laboratory, he withdrew the master key and opened the door. Groping in the dark, he found the light switch and flipped it. Nothing. Again he flipped the switch up and down — still nothing. Falling back against the wall, he cursed. "Why can't there be some damn lights?" he muttered repeatedly. After all, wasn't he doing God's work — saving His creation? The least He could do was provide a little light! The candles, he suddenly remembered. Nicholas, his lab assistant, always kept candles in the front closet in case of a power failure. Groping along the wall, he found the closet and after a bit of rummaging around, found a large candle but no matches. "Damn," he muttered again. If only he had waited another week to give up smoking, then he would still have his lighter. Matches, matches, he repeated over and over. Where could he lay his hands on some matches? Of course, he finally realized, the laboratory. Every laboratory was equipped with burners and strikers. With his candle in hand, he carefully negotiated his way through the maze of desks and computer stands to the laboratory door located at the back of the office. It was the largest and most sophisticated laboratory in the complex. Indeed, it was the most advanced research facility in the nation and one in which some of the best scientific minds in the world had labored to advance mankind's understanding of life and existence. How unfortunate, he thought while unlocking the door, that Danielle had chosen this laboratory for her unholy experiments. News of this could seriously cripple the Institute's ability to continue or launch future studies.

Stepping inside, he felt his skin grow cold. Normally the laboratory was cool, but not this cool. And too, a putrid stench permeated the air, a smell not unlike that in the substructure. Panic seized him momentarily before he remembered that Danielle had been locked in the laboratory most of the day. Evidently, the foul smell lingered longer in the closed atmosphere of the lab. Wells relaxed, and although cold he could feel himself perspiring profusely. The thought of being trapped here in the dark with Orien was more than he could handle. But it couldn't be; he had left the creature behind in pain and seriously crippled. Undoubtedly, Danielle was attending to him in the substructure at this very moment. Still, there was no time to lose. Eventually, they would have to come looking for him. Wiping his forehead, he continued his search for the burner and striker. In the darkness, he used his hands to sweep the length of the tabletop nearest him until he found the burner. A moment later, he had located the striker. Following the end of the hose, he found the gas valve and opened it while igniting the gas with the striker. A *bright orange flame burst forth and sputtered wildly before being brought under control with a few turns of the gas intake screw.*

Standing in the faint, shadowy light of the room, Wells gazed at the pale blue flame, mesmerized by its flickering movements. Unexpectedly, the light fluttered violently as an onslaught of cold air rushed past. Cupping his hand, he protected the flame from being extinguished and then raised the burner to high seeking to find the source of the air rush. To his surprise, he saw that one of the large panes of window glass had shattered, leaving a gaping hole. He stood, contemplating the situation. How had this window, so high above the ground, broken? In the dim light, he surveyed the area surrounding the broken window. There was nothing, not a bird or object accounting for the breakage, only the sight of broken glass as it lay about the floor and countertops. Suddenly, he sensed it, an ominous and powerful presence that seemed to fill the entire room. Overwhelmed by fright, he turned quickly, and in the dim wavering light he saw the unbelievable—Orien.

The monster held its mangled hand up for Wells to see and waved it about. Splattered blood from the severed fingers rained down its arm. Then, in quick steps, Orien moved in for the kill. Without thinking, Wells hurled the burner at the creature and rolled to the side. Instantly, the room went up in flames as the hose to the burner tore, releasing gas that was ignited by the open fire. Orien reared back in fright as a wall of flames crossed the room along the gas pipe. Although he had not deliberately planned it, Wells found himself on the vault side of the laboratory where Danielle had stored the embryos. Still, he needed time. Picking up a large beaker of acid, he hurled it at Orien on the opposite side of the flames and shouted in victory as the glass shattered and spilled its contents over the creature. Orien's eyes widened in pain. Wells pivoted quickly and made his way to the large refrigerated vault. Once inside, he gathered all the test tubes of frozen embryos and placed them into a box before turning to confront his final problem—how to escape the room. Both Orien and the fire stood between him and the exit.

Scanning the wall, he noticed a fire extinguisher. A plan quickly formed in his mind. Using the extinguisher, he could clear a path across the wall of fire and once on the other side, if Orien attacked, the extinguisher could serve as a weapon. But, would carbon dioxide be enough to hold back Orien? He had no choice—time was running out. Grabbing the extinguisher, he aimed low and laid down a steady stream of the chemical in front of him. With the embryos tucked securely under one arm, he slowly edged his way forward until safely on the other side. Several rows of laboratory desks separated him from Orien. He hoped the creature's preoccupation with the acid would allow him to cross the fire unnoticed. If so, he just might be able to slip out of the door without being seen.

That was not the case. Catching sight of him, Orien bellowed defiantly before grabbing a chair and hurling it. Wells ducked, and when he looked up he saw Orien leaping across the rows of laboratory desks in an effort to get to him. Placing the box on the floor, he grasped the extinguisher firmly and waited. Was there enough chemical left to deal a disabling blow to the creature? He prayed and waited and then, at the last possible moment, he released the extinguisher's contents into Orien's face as the creature attempted to reach him. It worked. Orien fell backward, stunned and momentarily blinded. Wasting no time, he threw the extinguisher aside, grabbed the embryos, and headed for the door. Once outside his office, he dropped the box and quickly inserted his keys into the heavily reinforced steel door. Turning the lock he hissed, "die, you son-of-a bitch, die." Then, picking the box up, Wells raced down the hall with the embryos secured tightly under his good arm. He thought about tossing the box into the fire, but decided not to at the last moment. Orien, though seriously injured, seemed to possess almost supernatural recuperative powers and might well have retrieved them.

Once inside the elevator, he put the box down, released the hold button, and then pushed the lobby button. Leaning back, he waited for the elevator to begin its descent, but nothing moved. Again he pressed it, and still nothing happened. Was it the relay switch? Suddenly, it occurred to him—the fire. The elevator was programmed to cease operation during fires to force occupants to use the stairways. It was a safety feature that could not be bypassed as he had done with the sprinkling system. The stairway was his only means of escape. Picking up the box, he started back the way he had come, but stopped. Crashing against the laboratory door was Orien. The window was broken and though Orien could not squeeze through it, the creature bellowed madly when catching sight of him clutching the embryos. Indeed, the mere sight of the embryos seemed to breathe new strength into the creature. What now?

RING! Startled, his head popped up instantly. Again, the phone rang and he quickly picked it up. "Phillip Wells," he announced.

"Dr. Wells," responded a woman's voice, "this is Marlene. One moment and I'll connect you with Dr. Cannon."

"Thank you," replied Wells. Looking at his watch, he realized that he had been asleep for more than an hour. Perspiration rolled down his face. It was that damn dream again. Using his coat sleeve, he blotted his forehead, eyes, and neck.

"Phil," it was Dr. Cannon's voice, "I understand you want to talk with me...something about a desperate situation?"

"Yes, Dr. Cannon. I'm afraid I've learned something that could ruin the Institute. Last night after hours I..."

"Listen, Phil," interrupted Cannon, "if this is as serious as you indicate, perhaps you'd better come over to my office."

"Of course, Dr. Cannon, I'll be over in a few minutes." Wells put the phone down and gathered some papers together. A moment later, he was out his office door.

The Institute was housed in a building with twin towers. Dr. Cannon's office was located in the tower opposite his own office. To get to it, Wells was required to ride the elevator down to the third substructure, take corridor C-4 over to the other tower, and then ride the elevator back up to the sixteenth floor of the other tower. Corridor C-4 was abandoned at this time of the evening. As he quickly walked its length, his mind flashed back to his reoccurring dream. It was uncanny how closely this corridor resembled the one where he was chased, repeatedly, by Orien. He felt his skin grow suddenly clammy. Looking over his shoulder, he quickened his pace. Entering the elevator, he hurriedly pushed the button and a sense of relief came over him as the doors slid shut. Shaking his head, he laughed with amusement at his silly behavior.

In no time he was at Dr. Cannon's office. Marlene was putting on her coat and getting ready to leave when he entered the foyer. Looking up, she smiled pleasantly and told him to go in unannounced as he was expected. Nodding, he reached for the door and opened it. At the desk sat Dr. Cannon. By the window, with her back turned and peering out, stood Danielle. Dumbfounded, Wells froze. He glanced at the CEO and then at Danielle.

"Have a seat Phil," Dr. Cannon said. "I think it's time we all have a little chat." Danielle turned, rounded the desk, and then sat to one side of it. Though he could have selected the center chair next to Danielle, Wells chose to sit opposite the woman in the smaller, less comfortable one positioned at the other corner of the large mahogany desk.

Dr. Cannon removed his glasses and sat them down in front of him. He was a big man. Not heavy, but tall, with thick silver hair and strong features. "Look, Phil," he spoke softly, "we have a problem."

"Damn right we have a problem," commented Wells. "And a serious one. I have no idea what Dr. Parker has told you, but I'm sure it's not the truth about what's going on in her laboratory."

"I'm fully aware of Dr. Parker's experiments," responded Canon briskly.

"No, I don't think so," replied Wells. "Not the Del-Phi project."

"I told you," interrupted Danielle, speaking in a voice bordering on hysteria. "He knows everything. The confidentiality of our work is completely breached; we face total exposure."

Wells watched in horror as the CEO tried to calm Danielle. It was now apparent to him that Cannon not only knew about her work, but was an active participant in the attempt to shield it from public knowledge. "I can't believe what I'm hearing. You don't object to this type of work?" asked Wells accusingly.

"What's there to object to?" asked Cannon calmly. "This isn't the first time that embryonic tissue has been used experimentally, you know that Phil. It's done in fertility work all the time."

"Wrong!" argued Wells. "Del-Phi is delving into areas untouched by science. You're using cross species genetic engineering to introduce animal traits into humans. For Christ's sake, you're attempting to alter the genetic code of the human species. And worse, the goddamn military is running the program! What the hell are they looking to create—a mutant warrior?"

"Phil," calmed Cannon, "Dr. Parker's work is only with aborted fetal tissue. No one is looking to create anything—it's purely scientific exploration."

"That's a lie and you know it," countered Wells. "Sure, Phase I of the program was with aborted fetal tissue, but Phase II is with active human embryos. You just laid the groundwork in Phase I, now you're ready to see if you can get normal cell division after the infusion process. Have you considered the ethical questions here?" Wells put a hand to his forehead. "And what about Phase III? Are you going to let this aberration of human life mature?"

"Phil," Cannon said calmly. "You're beginning to sound like a paranoid. Trust me, there is no Phase III."

"Even if I could believe that," answered Wells, "it still doesn't excuse playing God with active human embryos. We're talking about human life here, not chicken eggs."

"Wrong," responded Danielle. "Human life begins at birth, not at conception—that's the law. That's why the courts allow abortion, remember?" Wells stood staring at Danielle. It was obvious that he was less than sympathetic with her comments on abortion. "Look," Danielle quickly offered, "I know that you have strong reservations on abortion, but try to think of it scientifically. We need this research."

"Need?" laughed Wells. "No, Dr. Danielle Parker needs this research—to feed her discovery ego."

"True," she replied in response. "I'll admit it—I would like very much to make history. But that doesn't alter the fact that human-kind needs this research."

"How can you seriously believe that?" laughed Wells caustically.

"I'm very serious. Look around you, what do you see?" Without waiting for an answer she continued, "I see a species in decline. For the whole of mankind's existence on this planet nature has labored to create the perfect species through natural selection. Good traits are rewarded with survival; bad traits are weeded out through death. Cruel as it may be, the process insures that only the strongest, the fittest, pass their genes on to succeeding generations. But now, in the last three hundred years, our science has virtually brought man's evolution to a halt. Modern day technology and medicine protects the sick, the weak, the mentally deficient to a point that they live long enough to pollute the human gene pool through reproduction. That might seem to be a harsh assessment, but the truth is that, genetically speaking, humans are no longer advancing; we're regressing. We're becoming weak, ineffective, unable to respond to the challenges of the environment in which we live. That's where we come in. We present new solutions to new challenges."

"By polluting man's genetic code with animal genes?" questioned Wells.

"Why not?" responded Danielle. "Why shouldn't we take advantage of something that is clearly superior to our own genetic make-up? It's not that revolutionary of an idea. After all, haven't we transplanted animal organs into humans to sustain life?"

"In rare cases," replied Wells.

"Maybe," admitted Danielle. "But, what was the exception yesterday is the norm for tomorrow. That's the way science works. And it just may, someday, save our species from extinction."

"Spare me the melodrama, Dr. Parker," smirked Wells.

"No, wait," she said. "I can give you an example. Isn't it true that we face certain viruses and bacteria for which we have no immunity?" She paused briefly to insure that she had the man's attention and then offered, "Like AIDS."

"True," Wells admitted.

"Well," she continued. "We both know that some animals, despite the fact that they harbor the virus, do not develop AIDS. Apparently there is something within their genetic code that protects. What if we were able to unlock this secret and then incorporate it into our genetic code? We might be able to eliminate a threat to our existence."

Wells opened his mouth to protest, but Danielle interrupted. "I know what you're going to say, but what about other diseases lurking around the corner? Bacteria and viruses continue to mutate. We have no way of knowing what threats we face in the future. Our work may someday be man's last hope for survival."

"Or destruction!" rebutted Wells.

"Meaning?" questioned Danielle warily.

"The military," Wells answered. "Why do you think the military is interested in this type of research?"

"Initially, I had suspicions," admitted Danielle. "But then, the more I thought about it, the more I came to understand the practical necessity of this research. You must know that the Russians are doing this type of work. What if they, or some other country, are able to produce a virus to which no immunity exists with the exception, of course, that which they are capable of providing? My God, we would be defenseless— our freedom, our lives, our children's lives, would be at stake. To do nothing now while we have the time, is inexcusable." Looking up at the clock, Danielle gasped. "I have to go. We're at a critical stage in the lab." Quietly, so Wells couldn't hear, she spoke a few words to Cannon and then departed, leaving the two men together.

"I don't know," muttered Wells. "I just don't know about all of this."

The older man rose from his chair and limped towards the window. "What I wouldn't give to have been born a hundred years from now. Maybe, Danielle would have discovered a way to rid me of this damn arthritis," he joked.

"Excuse me for saying so, sir, but this is a helluva lot more serious than your arthritis."

"True," Cannon said reflectively. "You are right about that, Phil, but then you've got to look at the big picture."

"Big picture? And I suppose you and Danielle have the big picture, huh?"

Dr. Cannon sighed heavily. Then, as if suddenly struck by an idea, he patted Wells on the shoulder, "Come out on the balcony. There's something I want you to see." Moving slowly to the sliding glass doors, he disappeared into the night air.

By the time Wells stepped out, Cannon was already standing at the railing. Cautiously, he walked towards Cannon and placed one hand firmly on the iron pipe railing. He had a strong aversion to heights and usually avoided placing himself near high-rise windows or balcony edges. Now, he stood sixteen stories high, peering over the railing, and was unable to see anything but blackness below. "No, no, don't look down, look up," instructed Cannon, pointing to the sky. It was a clear night and the heavens were ablaze with distant suns. "Beautiful, isn't it?" said Cannon. Wells nodded in agreement, but said nothing. The two men stood gazing upward for a moment without talking. Then, Cannon was first to speak. "Tell me, Phil, what do you see?"

The younger man looked at his boss. His expression was one of confusion.

"Up there," replied Cannon again, pointing to the sky. "What is it that you see?"

"Stars," he answered. "I see stars."

"Yes, I know," he acknowledged. "But, beyond the stars, what is it that you see?"

Wells looked back to the sky searching momentarily before turning to Cannon with his answer. "I can't see beyond the stars, sir. Nobody can—it's too far."

"Of course," admitted Cannon. "That's the point I'm trying to make here. We live in a universe so immense that we can't see beyond our own galaxy. We know something must exist out there, but we haven't a clue what it might be. And without that knowledge, we have no way of knowing what challenges the human race is going to come up against in the future. We have to push science to its limits. We must find answers, not only for survival, but to satisfy our curiosity—it's our nature. It's the way God made us."

"God? You think God wants us to tinker with His creation?"

"Why else would He have given us the intellectual ability and the tools to get the job done?"

A silence fell between the two men. Finally, Cannon spoke. "Think about the things we said here. I think you understand how important it is for this project to remain secret. You do understand that it's classified, don't you?"

Wells nodded.

"Good," Cannon replied, walking him to the door. "Try to get some sleep—you look utterly exhausted. We'll discuss this some more tomorrow."

Phillip Wells nodded. Leaving the Institute he went directly home. Cathy was asleep by the time he arrived. He decided not to wake her. He was too tired to talk anyway. He slipped quietly into bed next to her and closed his eyes.

Yes, what now? He was trapped. He couldn't use the elevator and Orien blocked his way to the stairs leading down to the street. He searched for an alternative escape route. With the exception of the stairway leading to the roof, there was none. Getting to the roof was his only hope for survival. Tightening his grip on the box, he headed in that direction. Bounding up the stairs, in strides of three steps each, he reached the door in a matter of moments. To his relief it was opened. Unlike the interior doors of the building, this one was stronger, doubly reinforced and without windows. Slamming it shut from the outside, he flipped the locking lever that could only be released from the opposite side with the proper key. No sooner had he finished, and with his hand still touching the locking lever, the door buckled in a thunderous crash.

Stunned by the impact, Wells stumbled backward, tripping over some oil buckets that had been stacked near the door. The contents of one spilled, soaking the back of his clothing. Recovering the box of embryos, he quickly rose to his feet only to fall once again as his knees buckled with the pain stabbing at his shoulder. Fearing the worst, he opened his jacket to find blood seeping across his shirt. Without looking, he knew that his collarbone had broken free and punctured the skin. Understanding what had to be done, he struggled to his feet in a hunched position and reaching behind his back with his good arm, he grabbed for the other elbow. After taking three short breaths and exhaling, he took one final holding breath and in one movement jerked his elbow hard across his back while thrusting his shoulders up and back. The pain was instant and excruciating and he screamed as the bone slipped back beneath the skin and into place. The hinges to the door were beginning to give under the enormous force of Orien's strength. Grabbing the embryos, he began to circle the rooftop searching for another way to escape. Far below, he could hear the sirens of the fire trucks making their way to the Institute. They would arrive too late to help him. He would have to save himself.

The door tore free from its hinges and crashed to the floor where it lay in a crumpled heap of twisted metal. Wells closed his eyes, agonizing over his fate. Realizing it had the man trapped, Orien moved slowly but steadily toward him. With each step Orien took, Wells moved backward. Suddenly, the creature stopped as if sensing something. It was Danielle's presence. Emerging on the rooftop of the Institute's opposite tower, she screamed in delight at what she saw. Orien began to shriek and stamp its feet in childlike fashion on seeing Danielle. "Live!" she screamed, pointing at Wells.

An ugly determination came over Orien as it turned back toward him. "L-I-V-E," it uttered, almost letter-by-letter. Alternatives began to flash through his mind. He could toss the box of embryos to the side and then when Orien moved to retrieve them he could bolt for the door. But, then Danielle would have won and besides, once the embryos were secured, Orien would be free to chase him down. On the other hand, he could throw the embryos off the building to the street below, but he was absolutely certain that to do so would mean that he would soon be following them down. No, the concluded, the embryos were the only things standing between life and death. Edging back, he neared the ledge, a four-foot high concrete wall skirting the perimeter of the rooftop. Working his way along the wall, he came to the place where the two towers were joined by a giant six-foot pipe. Constructed as a power connection between the two towers, it was his last desperate hope. Hoisting himself up onto the flat wall, he stood waiting for Orien's approach and then, just as the creature arrived, he stepped down and out onto the pipe. Teetering precariously in the strong winds, he fought desperately to regain his balance. The creature watched as he jerked back and forth before securing himself on the pipe's smooth curvature.

Orien lunged at his ankles several times, but each attempt fell short. No matter how hard it stretched, it found him just beyond its fingertips. "That's right, big boy," taunted Wells. "To get to me you're going to have to come out here with me." It was almost as if the creature understood. Effortlessly, it raised its body up and onto the concrete ledge.

"Sure, big boy," he said almost amused, "that's the easy part. Now, let's try the pipe." To his surprise, Orien stepped out without difficulty. Standing astride the pipe in a bow-legged fashion, with its feet clamped tightly to the sides of the pipe, the creature used its massive strength to maintain balance. Wells was trapped. Caught between Danielle and Orien and with the ground sixteen stories below him, he had only one trump card left to play—the embryos.

"Give it up," screamed Danielle, "hand the embryos to Orien and you'll live. He only wants what gives him life."

It was now or never. Taking the box of embryos, he held them out in front of him tempting the creature. "Live," he uttered slowly. Orien edged closer, so close that he was almost within grasp of the box. At the last moment, Wells edged back. The two stood at arms-length, their eyes locked on each other. To Wells, Orien's gaze was one of confusion, a look that appeared almost human. "Live?" he asked, breaking eye contact. Orien moaned as he held out his good hand. "Then Orien must risk his life for it—catch!" he commanded, tossing the box to the creature's damaged side and just far enough so as to make it believe there was a chance. Instinctively, Orien lunged high and backward in a vain attempt to save the embryos and, in doing so, slipped from the pipe.

"No!" screamed Danielle in horror from the opposite side.

Turning carefully so as to see her, Wells announced his victory. "The nightmare has ended. It's over, Danielle." Her eyes widened suddenly and at the top of her voice she cried out Orien's name. Wells turned and peering through the darkness saw Orien clinging to the side of the building twenty feet below. Bleeding profusely, and with one leg broken, the creature attempted to pull itself up the wall to the safety of the rooftop.

Recalling the oil buckets, Wells made his way back to the wall, threw himself over it, raced to the stairway, and grabbed a full bucket of oil before returning to the wall. Looking over the edge he located Orien, near exhaustion and desperately attempting to save its own life. Carefully, he positioned the oil.

"God, no!" pleaded Danielle. "He's broken; he can't harm you. Mankind needs him."

"For what?" demanded Wells.

"Within Orien lies the answer to existence. Destroy him and you destroy mankind's chance to unlock the secrets of genesis."

"To what end will such knowledge serve mankind?"

"A better world," replied Danielle.

"And the risks?"

"What risks? There can be no others like him. Like life itself on this planet, his creation was a billion to one chance reaction. Without the embryos, he cannot reproduce; Orien is the last."

Orien was less than three feet from the top now. Sensing Wells was wavering, Danielle pleaded, "If not for mankind, then for life itself."

"What right does Orien have to exist?"

"All that is conceived has the right of life...."

BUZZ. Wells sprang up to a sitting position in his bed as the alarm clock broke the morning silence. Reaching over he turned it off and slumped back into bed. His pajamas, drenched in sweat, clung tightly to his skin. Closing his eyes he ran his fingers through his wet hair.

"Rough night, huh?" commented Cathy, as she watched her husband.

"Yeah, real rough."

"Same dream?"

Without looking up, he nodded.

"Tell you what," responded his wife, "you jump into the shower and I'll get breakfast started. Maybe we can talk before you head to work."

"Sure," he said, getting up from the bed. Slowly, he staggered to the bathroom while Cathy headed down the stairs for the kitchen. Opening the shower stall, he turned the hot water on and let the steam fill the small enclosure. He removed his clothes and stood naked before the mirror surveying his form. Next to Orien's it was a pitiful and neglected mass of tissue. But what man could compare to Orien? He entered the shower and let the water run over him while filling his lungs with the warm moist air. Out in the bedroom, he could hear the phone ringing. A moment later Cathy was tapping on the glass to get his attention. "Phil," she called, "it's Ernie on the phone." The woman waited for an answer before calling out again. "Phil, did you hear me?"

"Yes."

"What shall I tell him?"

Wells rested his head against the glass trying to think. The warm water showered down on his body engulfing him in a steamy, primordial atmosphere. Undoubtedly, it was the same environment in which Orien was conceived—perhaps man himself. He wondered about that.

New Dawn   Name_____

Instructions: read each statement before coming to class. Indicate your response by circling "agree" or "disagree" at the end of the statement. In class, discuss the statement with your group and attempt to reach consensus. If consensus is impossible record your vote and write *your* individual response to the statement in three or more complete sentences.

1. Inevitably, science will create a human being. Agree or Disagree. **Group Vote: Agree_____ Disagree _____**

2. Once science creates new technology there is nothing anyone can do to prevent its implementation. Agree or Disagree. **Group Vote: Agree_____ Disagree _____**

3. If science finds a way to cure human diseases by combining our DNA with that of animals, it has an obligation to do so. Agree or Disagree. **Group Vote: Agree_____ Disagree _____**

4. The trouble with scientific technology is that the rich will use it to advance their own self-interests at the expense of the poor. Agree or Disagree. **Group Vote: Agree_____ Disagree _____**

5. We have no right to tinker with our genetic structure. This is God's work. Agree or Disagree. **Group Vote: Agree_____ Disagree _____**

6. You simply can't trust the government when it comes to genetic research. Agree or Disagree. **Group Vote: Agree_____ Disagree_____**

7. Unless we put a stop to experiments in altering our genetic structure, humans will become obsolete. Agree or Disagree. **Group Vote: Agree_____ Disagree_____**

8. The money spent on most genetic research would be better spent improving the lives of the poor. Agree or Disagree. **Group Vote: Agree_____ Disagree_____**

9. There is really nothing wrong with using human embryos in genetic research since life begins at birth not at conception. Agree or Disagree. **Group Vote: Agree_____ Disagree _____**

10. For the sake of national security we need to continue our genetic research. Agree or Disagree. **Group Vote: Agree_____ Disagree_____**

Question # 1: If you were Phillip Wells would you attempt to put a stop to Danielle's research? Why?

_____
_____
_____
_____
_____
_____
_____
_____
_____
_____
_____
_____
_____
_____
_____
_____
_____
_____
_____
_____
_____
_____
_____
_____
_____
_____
_____
_____
_____
_____
_____

Question # 2: Do you feel that more good or harm will come from experiments that alter our DNA structure? Explain your answer.

Playing God

Nancy stood looking out of her kitchen window. Just moments earlier she'd been washing lunch dishes that the kids, who had disappeared to play baseball and tennis and who should have know better, had left for her to do. But she had been distracted by the sound of voices from across the way. From her vantage point in the kitchen, she could see directly into Mary and Jim's backyard. As was usual for any Sunday afternoon, Mary, hugely pregnant with their fourth child, was probably in the house cooking a lavish meal for her wildly growing and constantly starved family. Jim, in the backyard either splashing in the pool or playing ball with his three boys, was keeping them out of her hair while she fussed in the kitchen. Today, the horseplay centered on some version of a stickball game where Jim's rules kept the boys either laughing loudly or arguing good-naturedly.

As she stood watching, Nancy remembered the dozens of times she had looked out across the fence and marveled at what a wonderful father Jim Shepard was. From the time his boys had been born, he had carted them with him everywhere he went. Proudly they were strapped into their car seats while he made the rounds to do his weekend chores. No matter how little they were, they were welcome to help him do yard work or paint or work on the family cars. He seemed, to Nancy, to be the perfect father with the patience of a whole tribe of saints. She hated to compare him to her own husband, Tom, who was a good father, but she couldn't help it. When comparing the two men, Jim won any father contest. Hands down.

As she watched the four males playing and laughing she remembered back on some of the hysterical moments she had witnessed over the past eight years from her kitchen window. Or from her deck where she loved to sit and sip her tea and look out at her little world after a hard day's work. She thought about the time all four of them were out "mowing the lawn." She had to smile even though she rarely felt like smiling when she thought about the Shepard family these days. In her mind's eye, she saw a clear picture of Jim, constantly looking over his shoulder, with his power mower cutting neat diagonal lines across the big yard. And behind him, like baby ducklings, traipsed his sons. Eddie must have been somewhere between four and five, and Joey would have been about three, both pushing their toy mowers in a perfect line behind their father. And straggling behind them all, barely toddling, constantly falling in the uneven grass, was the baby, Matthew, determined to complete the hysterical picture. Or the time, earlier this spring, when it was still chilly outside, Jim was washing Mary's van. Matthew, then three and still dressed in his warm winter jacket, had picked up the hose and pulled the trigger. Unfortunately it was Jim, not the van, that got sprayed with the icy cold water. Mary laughed as she remembered the crazy dance that Jim did, clothes soaked and hair dripping, as he tried to get the hose from his son who just kept pointing the spray, full force, at his shocked father.

As she watched the children play with their father, Nancy realized that no matter what else she did today, she had to come to a decision on what had been plaguing her for the last two weeks. She felt more and more sure that by not confronting the problem she was copping-out and that if something did happen to any of the boys or Mary it would be, somehow at least, partly her fault.

The most difficult part for her was that she and Mary had become such close friends over the years. Just like Tom had become close friends with Jim. Even though Jim and Mary were ten years younger than she and Tom, the two couples often went out, shared many evenings together, and had even shared a summer cottage with each other for the past three years.

It seemed like the two families would be close forever. It wasn't until two weeks ago when Nancy had made the devastating discovery, that she realized that their friendship was about to come to a screaming halt. As a matter of fact, the way it looked now, she and Tom might well be coming to a halt themselves. She would have never anticipated that anything could divide them so completely. Through all of the years that they had spent together, all of their differences had been resolvable. And there had been some staggering differences. But they had allowed themselves the space to believe and act as each saw fit.

But this time it was different. As Nancy saw it, she and Tom had no choice. As Tom saw it, they had no choice. Unfortunately, the two choices were not the same. Worse, Tom had made it clear that she was not to do what she knew she had to do. What she knew she would do.

In the meantime, Mary had no idea what was going on. She only knew that somehow, she was losing Nancy as her friend because Nancy did not know what to do next. The two couples who normally saw each other many times over the course of two weeks had not been together at all in that period of time. Nancy was too busy, just leaving the house, would call later. Only she never returned her calls.

One part of Nancy cursed Tom for having told her the truth. Another part of her thanked God that he had. As she saw it, she was glad to know, even though she wished she would never have been told.

It was quite simple. Tom had come home from a golf game about three weeks earlier, clearly upset. As much as Nancy tried to get him to talk about what was bothering him, Tom had refused and begged off with a headache. That evening, the Shepards had come over to sit on the deck after all three boys were asleep. The deck made an ideal get-away. Jim and Mary were out of the house, away from the kids, and yet in clear eye and earshot of their home. The boys' bedroom windows faced the deck. When open, any sound was clearly audible, any lights being turned on, clearly visible. Many warm, dark summer nights were spent there, philosophizing or discussing world events and family problems.

That night proved to be different. Tom, usually the careful host, the sensitive conversationalist, was not himself. At first, he did not want to have the Shepards over. When Nancy told him that she and Mary had already made plans, he sulked around the house. Once they were all on the deck, Tom barely spoke. When he was forced into making a comment, it was either monosyllabic or a direct, unveiled jibe at Jim. The younger couple left early, clearly confused. Nancy, appalled at Tom's behavior, tried to get him to talk to her about what was going on. He refused.

Over the next days, little by little, Tom came around and seemed to be more himself. A few days after the deck incident, he went over to see Jim and the two men spent a couple of hours talking together while they worked on Jim's car. Nancy thought that whatever had happened between them was over and life was back on the usual track.

And so it seemed until Friday night two weeks ago when she got her first hint that something was very wrong. She and Tom had just gone to bed. The lights were out and the ceiling fan made quiet whooshing noises in the dark as it moved the sluggish air around the big, muggy room. They were both lying on their backs, staring into the darkness, lost in their own thoughts. Then, out of the darkness, Tom's voice asked, "What would we do if we found out that one of our friends was cheating on his wife?"

Nancy was startled. Usually they reserved such philosophical dialogue for when both were interested in a long, challenging conversation. Now, she was tired and really just wanted to run some fantasy stories about being wealthy and free to travel through her mind before she fell asleep.

"I don't know. I guess we'd have to ask ourselves if it was really any of our business," she answered.

"Yeah. You're right. I mean, they say that the wife usually knows."

"Well, I don't know if that's necessarily true," Nancy replied, warming to the conversation. "I just don't know if something like that is someone else's business. I mean, if you were cheating on me, I know I'd want to know; but I sure wouldn't want a friend to tell me. I mean think about how embarrassing that would be! I guess I'd prefer an anonymous letter, or something."

"Would you believe an anonymous letter? I mean, if one came in the mail tomorrow..."

"Hmm. You're right, I probably wouldn't believe it. I guess I just mean that one of my friends telling me something like that would surely ruin our friendship. First, I probably wouldn't believe it. Then, I'd hate her for knowing that about me. I'd think people were feeling sorry for me, or worse, thinking I was stupid. Third, I'd hate her for telling me even if I were glad I found out. Does that make sense? Probably not. But then all of this doesn't make sense. Where did this question come from anyway? Is one of our friends cheating on his wife?"

"Naw. Just forget it. It's all just stupid. You know. Something I saw on T.V. a couple of nights ago. Listen, just go to sleep. It's really getting late. We'll talk about it tomorrow."

Nancy lay silently lost in thought. This was really a very strange conversation. First, there was the taboo of talking about affairs. She and Tom had not talked about the subject dating back, what, 12 or 15 years, when she had become infatuated with Tom Sellick and her Tom had gone crazy with jealousy. She had been foolish enough to admit that maybe, just maybe, given the opportunity, she might consider giving old Mr. Sellick a run for his money. Second, Tom just wasn't the type of person to think about something like this as a result of some T.V. thing. Much less bring it up just as they were ready to drop off to sleep. Nancy couldn't help but wonder what this was all about and was determined to get to the bottom of it tomorrow.

The next day turned out to be the usual busy Saturday. The strange conversation of the night before got lost in a tangle of chores. Driving Josh to his baseball game, where he was once again injured, a trip to the emergency room for an x-ray of a bone that, of course, was not broken, and a dozen other minor calamities. But that night, as she was about to drop off to sleep, last night's strange conversation came back to her. Tomorrow, she decided, she would find out what that had been about.

These days, the boys slept later on Sunday mornings than they did. It was amazing how much sleep teenagers needed. Over coffee, Nancy brought up the conversation of a couple nights ago.

"Can we talk about the question you asked me just as we were ready to go to sleep a couple of nights ago?"

Too quickly, Tom replied, "Please. Can't we just forget it?" He wanted to let it go.

But Nancy needed to know what was going on. Her curiosity had gotten the better of her. She was sure that this had something to do with someone that she knew, and she wanted to know who, and what it was about.

"Look. We've talked about this before. I hate when you shut me out like this. I know something is going on. You're brooding about whatever it is. I want to know. But you won't talk to me and you're keeping me in the dark. I hate that and I think it's unfair. Talk to me!"

So Tom told her. The words just tumbled out. In some ways he was glad to be sharing it with her. It meant he didn't have to think about it alone. It took some of the pressure off. It meant that he didn't have to bear the responsibility of knowing all by himself.

So, he told her about when he and the guys had been playing golf a week ago and Joe Chambers told them about Jim Shepard, who he worked with. The same Jim Shepard who lived next door to them. The Jim Shepard that was his own best friend. The friend he thought he knew.

Tom took a deep breath and told Nancy that it seemed that Jim had a habit; one that he had had since his teens; one that Tom, since his two hour conversation with Jim while they worked on his car, knew he had tried to break. Time and time again he had tried to stop, but he never quite made it. In the end, he always went back. Sometimes he was clean for months. Other times he gave in, three or four or even five times a week.

Jim had prayed about it. He had sought counsel from his minister. He had even gone into therapy for a while, secretly, behind Mary's back, using money that they didn't have. He loved Mary. He loved her and the boys more than anything in the world. He would die without her. He couldn't bear to think about her finding out. But he couldn't stop.

When Tom had pointed out the danger that he presented to Mary, Jim had sworn that he was very, very careful. There was very little chance that something could happen to Mary. Didn't Tom know that he would never put Mary at risk? He would die rather than harm her.

"The problem, it seems," Tom told Nancy, "is that Jim is, well, I don't know any other way to say it, except to say, he's bisexual. He needs to see men. At lunchtime he heads for some place…. Oh God!"

In the end of course, it didn't turn out like he would have liked, with Nancy squarely in his corner, helping him deal with all of this. Rather, she went crazy with the news. He, who had all but lost his best friend. You couldn't be friends with a guy like that after you found out! No, Nancy yelled and asked him how he would put the rest of Jim's family, their friend Mary and the boys, at such risk. What about AIDS? Not to mention the numerous other sexually transmitted diseases. Did Jim have the right to put his wife and children, especially his pregnant wife and her unborn child, at such risk? And weren't they, as human beings, for God's sakes, responsible for their fellow human beings? Didn't Mary need to know this? Every day that she was unaware could be the day that Jim, knowingly or not, dealt her a deathblow in the form of AIDS. She had carried on for hours until he finally was driven out of the house to get away from her nagging.

Then, some days later, after he had absolutely forbidden her to tell Mary, she made the announcement that Mary was going to be told. One way or another. No matter what the cost, including the end of her own marriage to Tom. She, Nancy, was going to tell Jim she knew and give him a week to tell his wife about his "problem." At the end of the week, she was going to talk to Mary herself. Even if it meant the end of their friendship. Even if it meant the end of their marriage. As it stood, she said, she didn't know this new Tom. The old Tom would never have allowed something like this to happen. What was wrong with him anyway?

Nancy unceremoniously approached Jim outside while Mary was at the store. She told him in no uncertain terms what she thought about him and his behavior. And she announced that he had one week to talk to Mary before she did. Jim was devastated and asker her to reconsider. He promised her he'd stop. He told her he'd change. He begged her not to destroy his family, his life.

Nancy had refused to reconsider. In the week since their confrontation, Tom had spoken to her only to tell her she had better not do this if she expected their marriage to survive.

"You're the person who wondered whether this was any of our business. It's not!" he yelled.

Now, Nancy was lost in thought, propped up in the window staring out at the fun in the yard across the way. She was leaning on the window ledge with her elbows, her face propped in her hands, looking out. She knew that the week was up. If Jim had confessed, Mary would have called and asked Nancy for help. She was sure that Jim had not told. Mary was as unaware as ever that the man she loved, the man she crawled into bed with, the man to bathed and kissed and played with her children, was a potential killer in their midst. Today was the day she must tell Mary. But could she? Could she ruin her own marriage and her lose best friend all in the same day? Was she really so sure that this was the right, the only, thing to do? Wasn't this playing God?

She saw Jim look up at her from across the way. The smile died on his lips as he met her cold stare. He lowered his eyes and looked away. Nancy heard Mary call out that dinner was almost ready. The boys dropped their sticks and balls and raced for the door. Jim looked up at Nancy again before he turned away, shoulders slumped and head down, and followed his sons slowly into the house.

Playing God   Name_____

Instructions: read each statement before coming to class. Indicate your response by circling "agree" or "disagree" at the end of the statement. In class, discuss the statement with your group and attempt to reach consensus. If consensus is impossible record your vote and write *your* individual response to the statement in three or more complete sentences.

1. Despite everything else in Jim's life, he is a good father. Agree or Disagree. **Group Vote:**
    Agree_____ **Disagree** _____

2. If Jim and Mary divorce, the fact that Jim is bisexual should have no bearing on his right to obtain custody of the children. Agree or Disagree. **Group Vote: Agree**_____ **Disagree** _____

3. People have a right to their privacy. Nancy should butt out! Agree or Disagree. **Group Vote:**
    Agree_____ **Disagree** _____

4. Nancy has a greater obligation to her marriage than to her friend, Mary. Agree or Disagree.
    Group Vote: Agree_____ **Disagree** _____

5. There is no way that Nancy can know the true circumstances of Jim and Mary's relationship. Therefore, she should mind her own business. Agree or Disagree. **Group Vote: Agree**_____
    Disagree _____

161

6. Mary's life could be in danger. Nancy must tell Mary that her husband is having sexual relations with other men. Agree or Disagree. **Group Vote: Agree____ Disagree____**

7. The real problem in this case is the outdated sexual attitudes of society toward homosexuals. Agree or Disagree. **Group Vote: Agree____ Disagree____**

8. Getting into the middle of a friend's marriage is bound to destroy the friendship. Agree or Disagree. **Group Vote: Agree____ Disagree____**

9. Jim having protected sex with other men is no different than a heterosexual man having a safe extramarital affair. Agree or Disagree. **Group Vote: Agree____ Disagree ____**

10. Once Mary learns of Jim's problem, there is no hope for the marriage. Agree or Disagree. **Group Vote: Agree____ Disagree____**

Question # 1: If you were Nancy, what would you do? Why? Be sure to use information and theory from your textbook to support your decision.

_____
_____
_____
_____
_____
_____
_____
_____
_____
_____
_____
_____
_____
_____
_____
_____
_____
_____
_____
_____
_____
_____
_____
_____
_____
_____
_____
_____

Question # 2: In your opinion, do you feel that society should change its views toward homosexuality? If so, why? If not, why?

Same Song, Different Verse

Alice

"I forbid it! Absolutely, positively, no way! People in our family do not have abortions. Don't you understand? An abortion is an insult to God. If you are carrying a child, then you will have that child and you will raise that child. And furthermore, you will love that child. Do you understand, Alice? It's not as if we don't have the resources to provide. You will have that child! If you sin you pay the price and you, Alice, must pay the price."

"I can't go against your father. He's right. As much as I love you, I can't help you do something that is so wrong. I tried to warn you to be careful. I tried to warn you about men. But you didn't listen! How did this happen? Why, Alice? Why? How could you do this and spoil things for everyone?"

165

"Pregnant? What do you mean 'pregnant'? Who's the father? I know it's not me! And don't even dream of trying to pin this on me, either. Even if it were me, and I'm not saying that it is, what do you want from me? I don't have the money for an abortion. And I sure as hell am not going to spend the rest of my life taking care of a kid that I never even wanted and probably isn't mine to begin with! Besides, you're too young to get married or anything. I know I'm too young. Get rid of it!"

"I'm your best friend but I don't know what to do. How can I help you? I don't have the money to help with an abortion and even if you had the money, then what? Where do you go and what do you do when you get there? You're only 15, they'll call your folks and then what? They'll never let you have an abortion. I don't know what to do. Tell me what to do. Alice, maybe you should have the baby. You're folks have a lot of money. You and the baby will both be taken care of. It will have everything, just like you do."

"I've read about how they did them in the old days. Sometimes the women would take certain drugs. But I don't know what they were. We could probably find out at the library. Then there were chemicals that they put up inside themselves. But those were dangerous. I think. I know one of them was ammonia. But was it full strength or mixed with water or what? I know they used to use coat hangers, but I don't really know what they did with them, I just know they used them."

Alice sat propped up, back against the smooth oak finish in the window seat of her bedroom in her near perfect home and stared out into the brilliant sunshine with unblinking eyes that no longer see. Her long, skinny legs tangled underneath her on the satiny blue and cream colored fabric of the cushions still wet and sticky with dark red blood. The last of her life had drained away not more than three hours ago. The sun had not yet risen and it was still dark. Clouds of smoke gray mist had yet to be burned away by the first of the day's warmth. In the last moments she heard from a far away time the childhood taunt that followed her even into this other world. "Alice, Alice. Ugly, ugly Alice. Nobody likes Alice." She looked down at the red smear of blood on the white wire coat hanger. She remembered thinking that maybe if she had the baby, she wouldn't be lonely any more. But then she remembered how lonely she had always been in this house and she knew it would never get any better. Not for her and not for the baby. Maybe it was better this way. For both of them.

Debbie

Debbie had decided. She just wasn't going to argue anymore. This was her life after all! Who was he to try to make this decision for her? He was the one who broke his promise. No babies. He had always said that. No babies. Now, all of a sudden he wanted to be a father. What a jerk! He wanted to be a father so she was supposed to want to be a mother. To go nine months throwing up, getting fatter and fatter, and more and more uncomfortable, and in the end find herself in screaming pain strapped to some hospital table trying to deliver a baby she didn't want. She'd lived through the pregnancies of her friends, and they were all the same. Well, maybe not the same, but one worse than the other; and that didn't even include *after* the baby was finally born. That's when the real nightmare began. Home all the time, sick infants, defiant children, impossible teens. No, thank you. She had long since made up her mind, no kids. Now, one little sneaky sperm later, she was pregnant and Rick wanted to be a father...when he wasn't too busy with work or golf or being out with the guys. Great!

Rick was staring out of the window thinking about the best solution to this dilemma. Sure he'd always said no babies, but that's because he knew Debbie was so against having them. Now that she was actually pregnant with his child, he just couldn't let her kill it. The idea of being a dad appealed to him. Besides, he was 37. His company was doing well. They had a nice home. It was the perfect time to settle down with a child. He couldn't help it if something had gone wrong and now she was pregnant. Obviously, it was meant to be. Maybe this kid was going to grow up to save the world or something. Maybe he would invent some cure for a deadly disease. No way he was just going to stand by and let her kill it. No way.

The next day, Debbie was getting her coat on when the doorbell rang. She looked in amazement at the deputy that she found at the front door. He touched the brim of his cap. "Ma'am, are you Debra Jackson?"

Debbie mutely nodded her head. Was it Rick? Was he hurt? Or dead? She stared in disbelief as the officer spoke.

"I have a legal document here and you need to sign to accept delivery." As he handed her the thick envelope, she sighed with relief. At least it wasn't Rick. But who would be sending her a legal document? What was this about?

Silently she returned the clipboard and pen to the officer, stepped back and closed the door as she started ripping open the seal. She read in disbelief. A restraining order. Against her. Signed by a judge! She could not keep her appointment at the clinic. Instead, she needed to get a lawyer to defend herself. Rick, her husband, was suing to keep her from having an abortion.

After about an hour of just sitting in the recliner trying to decide what she would do next, she got up, grabbed her bag, and walked out of the door. Halfway down the walk she stopped and looked up at the house. This was it. The next time that she returned here she might be a criminal. She was fighting for the right to make decisions that concerned her own well being. One thing was for certain, things would never be the same between Rick and herself. While she was seeing the lawyer, she'd be asking for legal advice about the abortion, of course. But she'd also be taking the first steps to secure a divorce from the man she was in love with yesterday.

Kendra

"Shit!" Kendra stared at the blue ring at the bottom of the vial of urine.

"Shit, shit, shit, shit!" Her whispers echoed off the cracked, dirty white ceramic tiles of the walls and floor of the bathroom. Slowly, she dumped the contents of the vial down the toilet. Then, she crushed the packaging from the pregnancy test kit that she had stolen from the Walgreens down the street. Finally, she crammed it into the overflowing trash container that held soiled paper products. After she flushed, she tossed the small remaining butt of her cigarette into the swirling water and watched it go down the drain. After a few minutes, she let herself out of the small, cramped stall, threw on her ragged parka, and made her way out of the dirty restroom.

Once out on the street, the cold blast of winter air mixed with sleety rain hit her in the face almost as hard as the fact that she was in big trouble. At 18, she already had Lashawn to take care of, no job unless you called watching Terri's kids for almost nothing a job, no high school diploma, no future. The only thing she did have was what the state gave her. That kept her here in the projects where she'd been raped once already and had her apartment broken into at least once a month, as if there were anything there to steal. Now, another baby that she would have to keep because the state didn't pay for abortions and, no matter what those stupid television commercials kept saying, no one was going to want to adopt.

It wasn't that she was stupid. She knew where babies came from and how women got pregnant. She knew how to keep from getting pregnant. The pills that the clinic gave her were free, but they made her sick. Eddie didn't want to use rubbers. He hated them and always sweet-talked her into not making him use one. She used that cream she'd gotten from Walgreens, but apparently, it wasn't enough. "Shit."

Kendra told herself to calm down. The traffic light was red and the cars whizzing by threw wet slush all over the crowd standing on the corner waiting to cross the street. Okay. So what are my options? She might as well get used to it. She was pregnant. She could have the baby and be trapped longer. Lashawn was four and she had planned on going back for her GED at the community college as soon as he was in school all day. As it was now, she had almost no chance of ever getting a job that could make it possible for her to get on with her life. If she had this baby it would mean years of living in this neighborhood on handouts from the state. By the time she was able to go to school, Lashawn would probably be in a gang and his life would be ruined as well.

An abortion was the only answer. But how? She didn't have the money. She didn't know anyone who had the money. Welfare wouldn't pay for it. When her friend Sharon had been pregnant an old neighbor woman had aborted her. She was someone who would do it for free. But Kendra had heard about the pain. And that sometimes the women who went to her became very sick and ended up in the hospital. Some could never have children after that. One had even died.

It was hard to make a decision. She thought about Lashawn and how much she loved him. She smiled and could almost smell his clean, little boy smell. It wasn't that she hated kids. She just didn't think she could take care of another one. Most days she didn't think she could take care of herself! Have the baby?...or risk old Miz Cruz?...

"Shit."

Instructions: read each statement before coming to class. Indicate your response by circling "agree" or "disagree" at the end of the statement. In class, discuss the statement with your group and attempt to reach consensus. If consensus is impossible record your vote and write *your* individual response to the statement in three or more complete sentences.

1. Life begins at birth not conception. There is nothing wrong with abortion. Agree or Disagree.
   Group Vote: Agree_____ Disagree _____

2. The real problem in society is that too many women use abortion as birth control. Agree or Disagree.
   Group Vote: Agree_____ Disagree _____

3. Liberal abortion laws have promoted a new and dangerous attitude of permissive sexual relations for the young of our society. Agree or Disagree. **Group Vote: Agree_____ Disagree _____**

4. Stricter abortion laws would only increase the death toll by driving women to back alley butchers. Agree or Disagree. **Group Vote: Agree_____ Disagree _____**

5. If a man is required to pay child support, he should be able to prevent a woman from aborting his baby. Agree or Disagree. **Group Vote: Agree_____ Disagree _____**

6. Just like Alice's father said, "If you sin (play), you pay the price." Premarital sex is wrong. Agree or Disagree. **Group Vote: Agree_____ Disagree_____**

7. The real reason we have so many abortion is due to an overly permissive media environment. Agree or Disagree. **Group Vote: Agree_____ Disagree_____**

8. Teenagers should be able to obtain birth control without their parents knowledge. Agree or Disagree. **Group Vote: Agree_____ Disagree_____**

9. The use of state money (welfare) to pay for abortions should be banned. They got themselves into the mess, let them pay to get out of it. Agree or Disagree. **Group Vote: Agree_____ Disagree _____**

10. Teenagers should be allowed to obtain abortions without anyone informing their parents. Agree or Disagree. **Group Vote: Agree_____ Disagree_____**

> **Question # 1:** In which of the three cases, if any, do you think an abortion is justified? Be sure to list the reasons, whether for or against, for each of your decisions.

_____
_____
_____
_____
_____
_____
_____
_____
_____
_____
_____
_____
_____
_____
_____
_____
_____
_____
_____
_____
_____
_____
_____
_____
_____
_____
_____
_____
_____
_____
_____
_____

Question # 2: Present some suggestions on how our society might decrease the number of abortions. Of those you do suggest, state which would be easiest—politically, socially, and economically—to implement.

Sara

Sara Robbins walked briskly down 42nd Street heading north to the Grand Hyatt Hotel. The rush hour was just beginning and the sidewalk was quickly becoming a treacherous current of faceless people pushing and shoving their way past her in an attempt to shave a few precious minutes off their commute. Home to loved ones, she thought, that's where most of them were headed. She was going in the opposite direction. Up ahead she could see the hotel. David was probably already there, waiting for her arrival. Her mood brightened at the thought and she quickened her step. She was happy, very happy, for the first time in a long time. Yes, happy. Such a simple word but what an astonishing feeling. Without warning, a memory crept along the edge of her thoughts. She shuddered as she remembered last night's dream. What the hell had that been all about anyway, she wondered? Dark and foreboding, something had repeatedly called her name from somewhere outside of the scope of her vision. The shadows, or was it the fog, had prevented her from getting a better look at it. Its sound was low and raspy like an old jazz singer whose voice had been ravaged by a lifetime of booze and cigarettes. It had called to her, at least she thought it had, not in a threatening tone really, but one of sorrow and despair. She decided that she would have to think about it, but not right now. At this moment, all she wanted to think about was David. Yes, David, the beautiful, intelligent, and loving man she had met six months ago. She still couldn't believe that her department chair had recommended her, the newest member of the political science department, to represent the university at a seminar on international law sponsored by the Fullbright Foundation, a think-tank for government policy leaders. Now, at thirty-eight, she was on the fast track to a full professorship, a thought that pleased her enormously. Especially since she had entered her profession later than most of her colleagues without the responsibilities of a family.

David was waiting for her in the lobby. His face brightened when he caught sight of her. She quickly stepped into his arms. No words were needed. They simply turned and walked to the elevators. An hour later they lay in bed together, comfortable and complete. Their lovemaking had been as always—tender, loving, and fulfilling, both in body and in soul. For the first time in her life she felt fully alive. Surely, she thought, it must be the feeling of one who had, for one reason or another, wrestled life from a sure, slow death. Life now was exhilaratingly fresh and hopeful.

David nudged her softly. "I think it's time we go."

"I don't want to leave now," she moaned.

"Me neither, but I don't want you to be late. Our time will come."

"Really?"

"Yes, absolutely."

"How can you be so sure?"

"You taught me to love," he whispered. "Before you, I didn't think I would ever love anyone. I'm not even sure I believed in love. At times I was convinced it was a fantasy that existed in the minds of poets and songwriters. Other times, I entertained the thought that it did exist, but that I was too damaged to feel it. That was the worst of all feelings. Then I found you, and now I know that love exists. We'll be together. I just know it."

"I hope you're right, but I'm scared."

"Don't be," he said, kissing her lovingly. "Now, let's get you on your way."

Sara and David exited the elevator. They embraced one final time before she had to leave. It was then that she heard her name being called. Turning, she looked into the startled eyes of her best friend and neighbor, Cathy Hughes.

"Sara," said the woman breathlessly as her eyes shot back and forth from Sara to David. "It is you, isn't it?"

Sara could feel heat spread across her face as she frantically searched for a way out. There was none. Her expression foreclosed any possibility of lying. She hung her head, resigned to her fate. Looking up again she said, "Cathy, I would like you to meet David, my special friend."

The eyes of the woman widened in disbelief.

"Yes, it's true." Then turning, she said, "David, would you excuse us? I think Cathy and I need to talk."

"Of course. I'll call you tomorrow."

The two women watched as David disappeared out the hotel doors.

"Sara," pleaded Cathy, "I'm sorry. I didn't mean to pry. Jim wanted to have dinner here for our anniversary and I work close by so I thought I'd make reservations in person. Jim said he'd meet me for a drink if he could, but I got here a lot earlier than I thought I would so...God, I'm just rambling on, please make me stop!" Cathy pulled herself together. "Sara, I saw you and I didn't think. I should have walked away. I'm sorry, so very sorry."

"Don't blame yourself," Sara replied. "It's not your fault. I hope you have time for a drink so I can explain."

"A drink," muttered the woman. "I think I'll need more than one."

"Me, too," Sara admitted. "Let's go."

For the next half-hour, Sara poured out her story to her friend. She spoke of the emptiness of the last ten years of marriage to her husband, John. She described how she met David at the seminar, how it had all begun so innocently. How they had been assigned to the same follow-up committee that met twice a month to discuss current policy decisions. No, he had not pressured her. In fact, his behavior was beyond reproach. Years ago, he had been married briefly. It was a marriage he described as bloodless, one empty of happiness and intimacy. Then, after eighteen months of marriage, his wife had been killed in an automobile accident. The accident left him reeling from a variety of mixed emotions. He couldn't reconcile his grief with his relief. The guilt left him on an emotional roller-coaster ride that had almost destroyed him. It was she, admitted Sara, who had made the first move. Over time, she had felt drawn to him. She tried to dismiss her feelings as whimsical, the fantasy of an adolescent. But her desire for David grew stronger. Finally, she could think of little else and knew she would have to confront him. One way or another, she had to free herself from the uncertainty. Either he would reject her or reveal his own attraction to her. Confessing the inadequacy of words to describe their encounter she attempted to convey, as best she could, the pain and joy that resulted from that meeting. Joy in finding David's love for her was as strong as hers for him; pain in the knowledge that as much as she wished she was free to go to him, she was not. For weeks they struggled with their feelings and finally, when it was no longer possible to deny their destiny together, they became lovers. Resisting, she explained, was like unfurling sails in the midst of a hurricane.

Through it all Cathy listened intently without interruption. She was about to speak when a voice boomed from behind them. "Ah ha, a conspiracy!" Looking up they saw Jim, Cathy's husband, standing over them.

"A conspiracy?" mocked Cathy recovering quickly. "Surely, you are not referring to two innocent ladies having a drink together as a conspiracy, sir?"

"Don't give me that," he continued the play. "I'm on to your conniving ways."

Cathy stood and slipped her arm around her husband's waist. "Okay, you caught us. We confess to scheming against male domination. What's the penalty?"

"I'd say having to share dessert with me," he ruled. "I saw some scrumptious looking éclairs in the pastry shop."

Sara rose quickly. "I'd love to, Jim. But I have to pick up the boys today. You know, the ball and chain you guys have saddled us with."

Pointing his finger, he replied. "Alright, I'll grant a temporary reprieve. But I won't forget. You owe me an eclair penalty."

Sara smiled. She quickly hugged Cathy and whispered, "I'll call." Then she was gone.

Sara was putting the finishing touches on the evening's dinner. The sounds of her children rough-housing with their father drifted into the kitchen. Tears welled up in her eyes as she contemplated her situation. How was it possible to be so happy and yet so sad at the same time? After dinner, John cleared the table and began dishes while she got the boys' backpacks ready for school the next day and then tucked them into bed. Walking into her room, she picked up the phone and called Cathy. Her friend answered on the third ring.

"It's me, Cathy."

"Oh God, Sara," she whispered, "how are you?"

"Not so good. Do you have time for lunch tomorrow?"

"Yes, of course."

Sara went to bed early that night. In spite of her anxiety she fell asleep almost immediately. And then came the dream. . . .

It was dark, so very dark. She groped about with her arms and hands searching in front of her. Nothing she touched felt real. The air was wet, heavy, and pungent. Suddenly, she felt herself falling, not down to the ground, but through a long spiraling tunnel. She landed hard, but without pain. She stood. Looking up she could see a light shining from above where she had fallen. Though bright, the light was dispersed by a wet mist that hung heavy in the air. Turning in a full circle she tried to survey her surroundings. It appeared to be a hollowed out cave with large stone spikes driven deep into the earth. Each spike was covered with sticky membrane-like tissue. From the tip of each spike dripped a thick mucous-like substance. Suddenly, she felt the floor beneath her tremble as if the earth itself was afraid. The wind picked up, and then calmed. She felt trapped in the eye of a vast storm.

"Sara," called the voice she'd heard in last night's dream.

She spun around quickly—nothing.

"Sara," it beckoned again from somewhere behind her. Again, she pivoted only to find nothing. Again and again the voice hailed her, but no matter which way she turned

it remained, somehow, behind her.

"Who are you?" she cried. "How do you know my name?"

"I know. . . I know you, Sara."

"What do you want?"

"I want. . . I want. . ."

"What?" she screamed.

"You mustn't. . ."

"Leave me alone!" she shrieked.

"Sara, Sara, wake up," the voice was her husband's. "It's just a dream. Just a dream." The beating of her heart pounded in her ears with a deafening rhythm. Her night gown was soaked with perspiration. "Yes," she stammered, "a dream. Just a silly dream. . . ."

On the following day, when Sara arrived, Cathy was already sitting. A glass of Merlot sat in front of her. Looking down at her glass, she joked, "You know, Sara, you're gonna make an alcoholic out of me."

"Please," responded Sara, "let's do one problem at a time."

Cathy watched her friend grow deadly serious. "Tell me," she coaxed, "how bad is it between you and John?"

"Bad, really bad," sighed Sara.

"John hasn't been abusive, has he?"

"John?" asked Sara. "Heavens, no! He doesn't have an abusive bone in his body."

"Then I don't understand," her friend confessed. "Why?"

"I'm still trying to figure that out myself."

"Have you tried marriage counseling?"

"No, I haven't."

"Maybe that's a place to start," offered Cathy in earnest.

"I don't think so."

Cathy put her hand over Sara's. "Tell me why you don't think counseling will help."

"Because the problem isn't between us—it's me. The problem is me."

"I find that hard to believe, Sara," she countered. "You're the most loving, kind, and intelligent person I know. How could it be just you?"

"Trust me, Cathy. It is me."

"Then you're going to have to explain it to me."

"It's too complicated."

"You're telling me I'm too stupid to understand?"

"Of course not," Sara retorted. "It's just long and complicated."

Cathy leaned back in her chair. "I have the time," she said, pausing to sip her wine. "Let's have it."

Sara sighed, "You don't know much about my childhood, do you?"

Cathy shook her head.

"I didn't think so," she replied. "Anyway, it began in Carlyville, a small town in Missouri. It was a town filled with small minds and watchful eyes. It's the type of town that sucks the life out of people. You're born there, you live there, and you die there."

"I take it you didn't like it very much."

"I detested it."

"What about your folks?"

"Mom loved it. Dad hated it as much as I did."

"But he didn't leave?"

"He tried, but Mom wouldn't hear of it. Her parents lived there. But that wasn't the real reason. She was afraid of the world and Carlyville was comfortable. She said that if Dad left, he would leave without her and without us kids. She threatened to divorce him. Finally, he just gave up. But he didn't give up on us kids. Every chance he got, he told us to get out before it was too late, like it was for him."

"Is that where you met John?"

Sara nodded. "John was a dreamer. He had plans. He wanted out of Carlyville as much as I did. We started making plans early on in high school. We were coming to New York. John was going to train as an electrician, work for several years for seed money, and then we were going to start our own company. In between raising the children, I was going to work in the business—scheduling, bookkeeping, and sales. We were going to own the world."

"What happened?"

"For a while, everything went as planned. John became an electrician, we scrimped and saved, and finally started our own company. I had the boys and was preparing to begin working again when John came home one day and told me that he had closed the business. He said he didn't like the responsibility of being the boss, the extra hours of work, the hassles of dealing with clients."

"You had no idea, no warning?"

"None whatsoever," Sara confessed. "I didn't even see it coming. Anyway, we lived off our savings for a few months and then John went to work with Evans Electrical Company. He's been there ever since."

"You seem angry about that," said Cathy.

Sara thought for a moment before replying. "I don't think angry is the right word. Perhaps disappointed. On the one hand, he made a decision that affected both of us. It was my dream, too. On the other hand, he had a right to do what made him happy." She sighed. "And he did say he wanted to spend more time with his family. How can I fault him for that?"

"So that's what motivated your return to school."

"It was one part of it," answered Sara. "The other was that I was so bored with my life. In the beginning, I was just going to take a class or two, but that changed the minute I stepped into the classroom. People were alive with ideas. They were passionate about the world. They wanted to do great things. It was infectious. Suddenly, I found myself talking about events, places, and people from around the world. And, to my own amazement, I discovered I was good at it. I couldn't learn enough. One course led to another, and suddenly I was walking across the stage with a diploma in my hands. Twelve months later I walked again for my Master's and was accepted into a Ph.D. program. And then came the offer from the university—a position on the faculty. I thought I was dreaming. There I was a small town girl from Carlyville, on the faculty at a university.

Sara paused reflectively and looked into the eyes of her friend. "Marriage counseling is not going to solve this problem. It can't change who I am and it can't change who John is. I'm no longer the person he married. He's no longer the person I married. The only things we have in common are the boys and the house."

"Have you tried to bring him into your world?" asked Cathy.

"Many times," she replied. "He has absolutely no interested in anything outside of our home and his work. I've tried to get him to listen to world news on television with me or read the editorial section of the paper—something, anything we could discuss together. But he is just not interested. His reading is limited to the sports page and the only thing he watches on television, other than movies or sports, is the weather report."

"Do you think David might have something to do with how you feel about John?"

"I wish it were that simple, but the answer is no. My unhappiness began years before David. Meeting David forced me to confront my repressed feelings and needs."

The two women talked a few minutes more until Sara had to leave for class. Before going, she thanked her friend for listening. Cathy assured her that she would always be there for Sara whenever she was needed.

The plate on the door read Melinda Fremount, Professor of Psychology. Sara stood at the door and knocked lightly. From inside a voice called, "it's open." Sara turned the handle and stepped into the office. Melinda was at her desk. Spewed across the top were papers and journals. The woman removed her glasses and greeted Sara. The two women had met when Sara first came to the faculty. Melinda, being the unofficial chair of the professional women's support group at the university, had invited her to join the group. Melinda was a large, attractive woman with beautiful, stylishly cut, silver hair and striking blue eyes. "Sara," she greeted warmly, "what brings you to the mental ward?"

"This is hardly a mental ward," commented Sara looking about the spacious office.

"There are days," Melinda quipped. "Now, what can I do for you today or is this just a social visit?"

"I wish," confessed Sara.

"Oh, oh," Melinda murmured as she rose from her desk. "Let's sit here," she said directing Sara to two facing leather chairs with a coffee table between them. After settling in Melinda asked, "What's going on?"

Tears welled up in Sara's eyes as she began from the beginning. Melinda listened, nodding occasionally. When Sara finished, Melinda spoke. "And the bottom line is that you feel guilty and responsible, right?"

"How can I not feel guilty?"

"I see," commented Melinda. The woman searched Sara's eyes and then leaned forward. "Sara, I know this is hard for you. It's like you're caught up in an emotional storm being blown first in one direction and then in another, at the whim of a force much stronger than anything you can possibly imagine. In cases like this it's only natural that victims blame themselves."

"Victims?" questioned Sara weakly.

"Yes, you are a victim," repeated the older woman. "Think about where you grew up and the time in which you spent your childhood. How much attention was paid to girls? How much encouragement did you get? Boys were taught that the world belonged to them. They could be anything they wanted. The choices were much more limited for girls. We were expected to be kind, obedient, loving, and giving. Few girls coming out of small towns and those times were encouraged, or even allowed, to explore their true potential. From start to finish, our role has always been that of cheerleader for our brothers and boyfriends. For some women that was fine and they found happiness. But for many others, that one-size-fits-all world didn't work. I suspect that's what led you back to school where, in essence, you discovered yourself and in doing so you changed. You moved on and John was left behind because he didn't feel the need to change." Melinda stopped and looked at Sara. "Is all of this really a surprise to you?"

That night Sara pulled out her yearbook from high school and leafed through the pages. It had been years since she had revisited her past. Carlyville was as she had remembered it—dreary and confining. She was thankful for escaping its deadly grip. John had put the boys to sleep and, as usual, retired early for the evening. Putting her feet up on the sofa, she lay her head on the armrest and drifted off.

"Sara," called the voice. It was closer now, stronger than before.

"Go away," she begged. "Leave me alone."

"No, Sara," it rumbled, "come to me. Only I can save you."

"No!" she shouted. "I'm doomed. No one can save me." Ahead, a blue light appeared in the distance. She began to run hard but her legs were heavy and each step became more laborious than the last. In her mind she repeated, over and over, that this was dream. She attempted to will herself awake, but to no avail.

"Sara," called the voice, "embrace me. Only I can save you. . . ."

Much later, Sara rolled from her bed startling her husband. For the second time that night she awoke from the dream drenched by her own perspiration. Pulling the nigh gown off, she stood naked in the dark. She heard her husband fumbling for the light. "No, John, leave it off."

"What's wrong, Sara?"

"A dream. The same dream. I'm trapped in a cave. Something is chasing me. Something awful."

There was silence before her husband responded. "Maybe you should cut back on your work, huh?"

"I don't think it's the work, John."

"Well, I do. It was that way with me," he responded. From behind her she heard him roll over in the bed. A minute later he was asleep.

Raising the cup to her lips, Sara took a sip of the hot coffee as her friend waited patiently.

"I don't mean to pry, but I'm concerned for you," Cathy began. "How is it going?"

"With whom, David or John?"

"Both. Either."

"With David, it's as wonderful as it could possibly be. It's always been wonderful and in my heart I know it always will be wonderful. We share the same interests, the same concerns, the same need to reach out and make a difference in the world. We're perfectly matched. The only problem between us is that we both feel guilty about John." Sara sighed. "David's never been in this position before. When he was married, before his wife died, he valued being faithful, doing the honorable thing. As unhappy as he was, he believed in doing the right thing and he did it. He's not pushing me. He says it's my decision. But I know in his heart that he wants to put the secrecy and deception behind us."

"Hmm. Let's try something else. Have you tried bringing John into your life more?"

"Yes," she answered. "I brought some books thinking that if he began reading we'd have something to talk about, something more than just the kids, the bills, the house, the ordinary day-to-day stuff of life."

"And?"

"Not a page. The only reading that interest him is the sports page of the paper and some of the hunting and fishing magazines he subscribes to. Next, I suggested going out to the movies more often so we could talk afterwards. He's not interested in anything Hollywood has to offer except for an occasional Rambo-like movie. I even tried to get him to attend some of the events at the university."

"Did he?"

"A couple of times. But then he stopped. He told me he didn't feel comfortable around all the 'eggheads'. I tried to get him to take a course at the university. He asked me if they had courses on fly-tying."

"Fly-tying?"

"Yeah, you know," answered Sara, "for fishing."

"But have you tried to tell him how you feel about the relationship?"

"Oh, God!" exclaimed Sara. "Don't mention the 'r' word. He hates talking about the relationship," she said gesturing with her fingers. "One time when I tried to force the issue, I told him how desperate I felt, how I wanted our lives to change. How I wanted us to be more involved. I thought I had made some progress. The next day, he went out and bought me a fishing rod."

"A fishing rod?"

"Yes, a fishing rod," repeated Sara wearily. "I guess that he was trying, but he had no clue about what I was talking about. So we sat down again, and I tried again to communicate my needs, my hopes for us."

"Did you get through to him?"

"No," answered Sara. "Not at all. He sat there, listening and nodding his head. The next week when we were at his sister's house he quietly asked her at what age a woman usually goes through the change. I found out about it when she cornered me later in the evening and asked me if we were having problems. After that, I gave up trying."

"But what if you told John you were thinking about leaving? He might change."

"That's not fair to John. And, in the long run it's not a productive solution to the problem. Think about it. I put a gun to his head and force him to change. He might agree to save the marriage, but can you really force someone to change? John's comfortable with who he is and what he wants from life. Who am I to force him to change?"

"And David?"

"That's the problem," answered Sara. "Meeting David has made me feel lonely, really lonely. And more alone than I've ever felt before."

The expression on her friend's face showed confusion.

"I know it sounds crazy, but before I met David I was okay. Well," she recanted, "not really okay. I always had the sense that something was missing, a sense of being incomplete. But I was coping. I had my career and I had the boys. Then, David walked into my life, and suddenly, I knew what I was missing. I always laughed when people talked about soul-mates, thinking it was just words, hopeful fantasies of infatuation. But when I met David I knew instantly that he was my soul-mate. And, no matter how this turns out, he will be my soul-mate for eternity." Sara's eyes filled with tears. "And that's what makes me lonely, and alone, and afraid." She paused momentarily. "How do I live now? I don't want to hurt John, but I have this terrible emptiness in the way I live. I don't think I can go on."

Cathy sat contemplating her friend's words. Then she asked, "what about the boys?"

"What do you mean?"

"If you leave, will John keep the boys?"

A horrified expression crossed Sara's face. "God, no! They're my boys."

"They're John's boys, too..."

Sara entered the room as if in a fog. Her eyes were red and swollen.

"Well," greeted Melinda Fremont, "I guess I don't have to ask how you are today."

Sara attempted a smile, but it quickly vanished.

"Did you sleep last night?"

"Off and on," replied Sara.

"Did the dream come again?"

Sara nodded.

"Tell me."

"It started as always. I'm in spiral, falling. Around me there are lights, brilliant lights—red, green, yellow—as I fall." Sara paused. Her eyes were fixed on some point far in front of her. It was as if she had willed herself into a hypnotic trance.

"Are you still falling?"

"No."

"Where are you, Sara?"

"In his place."

"Whose place?"

"I don't know. He won't tell me."

"Can you see him."

"Yes, he beckons me to listen."

"What does he say, Sara?"

"He speaks of an impending disaster, a disaster worse than death itself. He pleads with me to think, to choose carefully."

Who is he, Sara? Can you see his face?"

"No."

"Is his face hidden from you?"

"No."

"Then why can't you see him?"

"I'm afraid. The fear is overpowering. I sense that to look is to die."

"Sara," commanded Melinda, "look up. See your tormentor."

"I can't! I can't." Suddenly Sara jumped from the chair. Running to the open window she gulped air frantically, swallowing it as if it was water. A moment later when she was more composed she turned to Melinda.

"I can't look! I'll never be able to look."

"If you did look, who do you think you'd see?"

"I don't know."

"You don't?" coaxed the woman.

"Maybe."

"Tell me."

"I can't be sure. But, I somehow sense it would be David or ...."

"Or?"

"Or my father."

"And you're afraid of the truth?"

"Yes," she replied weakly. "But I do know that I never want to go there again."

"Then you must choose, Sara," confronted her friend. "The dream won't go away until you choose."

"I know," Sara replied. "I've always known." Turning to the window, she gazed out onto the courtyard. In the west, dark and foreboding clouds gathered. On her face she could feel a cool breeze, playing troubadour to the storm's impending arrival. There would be wind, brilliant flashes of lightning, and then the rain, a hard rain that would cleanse the earth. She watched as the storm moved closer. Soon it would be on her. It was as inevitable as the decision she felt forced to make.

Sara   **Name**_____

Instructions: read each statement before coming to class. Indicate your response by circling "agree" or "disagree" at the end of the statement. In class, discuss the statement with your group and attempt to reach consensus. If consensus is impossible record your vote and write *your* individual response to the statement in three or more complete sentences.

1. Infidelity is wrong under any circumstances. Agree or Disagree. **Group Vote: Agree**_____
    Disagree _____

2. Melinda Fremount is right, Sara is the victim in this story. Agree or Disagree. **Group Vote:**
    Agree_____ **Disagree** _____

3. For the sake of the kids, Sara should give up her relationship with David. Agree or Disagree.
    Group Vote: Agree_____ **Disagree** _____

4. If Sara does leave John, he should get custody of the kids. Agree or Disagree. **Group Vote:**
    Agree_____ **Disagree** _____

5. It's impossible to be a good parent while being unfaithful to your spouse. Agree or Disagree. **Group**
    Vote: Agree_____ **Disagree** _____

6. Now that Cathy knows of Sara's affair, she is morally obligated to tell John. Agree or Disagree.
   Group Vote: Agree_____ Disagree_____

7. John's lack of attention to Sara's needs are the real problem in this relationship. Agree or Disagree.
   Group Vote: Agree_____ Disagree_____

8. If John and Sara do get a divorce, she should not be able to collect alimony. Agree or Disagree.
   Group Vote: Agree_____ Disagree_____

9. Given the social and economic constraints of our society, cheating is sometimes the only answer.
   Agree or Disagree. **Group Vote: Agree_____ Disagree _____**

10. Sometimes, no matter how hard people try, it's impossible to fix the problems in a bad marriage.
    Agree or Disagree. **Group Vote: Agree_____ Disagree_____**

Question # 1: If you were Sara, what decision would you make regarding your marriage to John? Why? Be sure to use information and theory from your textbook to support your decision.

Question # 2: Given modern society, what suggestions do you have to help people avoid divorce?

The Collar

This wasn't the way it was suppose to be today, cursed Tom Delany as he raced around the corner with his service revolver held high. Today was an off-duty day. Time he was suppose to spend with his wife and child. Now he was hot in pursuit, in civilian clothes, with no backup, and no radio. Ahead, the suspect frantically shoved his way through a mass of people crowding the sidewalk. Delany pursued in his wake trying as best he could to keep track of the gun in the suspect's hand. Over the roar of the streets and terrified screams he could barely hear his own voice shouting, "Police! Police! Out of the way!"

Delany knew he was fast but this guy was faster. His only hope was that the suspect lacked endurance. If so, the race was already over because Delany could run all day. No one could run harder, longer, or farther than Delany. All he had to do was keep the suspect in sight and before long the collar would be his. Ahead, the suspect stopped, looked back in his direction. For an instant their eyes locked—prey and hunter. Turning quickly to his left he bolted down a side street. The stop had cost the suspect precious seconds and Delany took advantage by closing the distance between them. No way could he lose the suspect now, thought Delany, but his main concern was the gun. He had to keep track of the gun.

Delany screamed for the suspect to give it up but he knew there was little hope for that outcome. Moments earlier the suspect had shot a man on the corner of Fifth and Broadway. Delany had witnessed the scene from the opposite street corner. He, with his wife and daughter, was on the way to a restaurant down the street when he heard an altercation break out between the two men, one well-dressed, the other in sweats. Suddenly, two shots rang out. The well-dressed man slumped to the ground. Delany's instincts took over despite cries from his wife not to intervene. It was his job. He had to act. Withdrawing his service revolver he raced across the street dodging traffic and screaming that he was a police officer. At first, the suspect stood over the fallen man as if stunned. Then, hearing Delany, he looked up and fled.

When Delany arrived at the scene of the shooting he realized two things. First, having been shot in the leg the wounded man was not in danger of dying. Second, the victim was Seth Stevens, a narcotics detective from the fifth ward.

"You get that punk and shoot him! Ya hear?" Stevens shrieked in pain, "Make him pay!" Delany nodded and headed in the direction of the suspect. It was only a matter of seconds before Delany located his prey and the chase was on.

Delany pushed himself harder. For a moment he wondered if he had underestimated the shooter. He was four blocks into the chase and running as fast as possible. By now, most suspects would have given-up or collapsed from exhaustion. In fact, Delany usually welcomed a chase because it tended to take the fight out of the suspect. But this guy was far from ready to give it up. He was going to be a handful, if he ever did get his hands on him. Suddenly, the suspect pivoted sharply to his left and took off down an alleyway where he disappeared into one of the abandoned buildings. Delany cursed as he watched the suspect slip from sight. Of all the possible scenarios, this was the worst. Now it was no longer a chase; it was hide-and-seek with the advantage shifting to the suspect.

Flinging himself against the building to the left of the door, he flattened his body into the aging bricks. He was breathing hard, too hard, he thought. Inside his chest his heart pounded against his ribs like a wild animal attempting to free itself from a cage. Images of his pleading wife begging him to give it up and walk away leaped to the forefront of his consciousness. In private moments other officers, his friends, had confessed to similar images as they faced life-threatening choices. He wiped the sweat from his eyes and pushed the thoughts from his mind. It was his job, he reminded himself again. He had taken an oath. How could he walk away and still wear the badge?

Leaning slightly to his right he quickly glanced inside the building before ducking back behind the safety of the bricks. Though dark, he could make out rows of old crates and empty 50 gallon steel drums stacked one on top of the other. The floor was covered with litter and streams of light beamed down from broken skylights. On the down side, it provided the suspect with plenty of places to hide. On the upside, it afforded him cover if he could negotiate his way around and over the litter to the first stack of barrels without being shot. He estimated the distance to be between fifty to sixty feet. Delany calculated his odds. If the suspect was directly in front of him he would be a relatively easy target. On the other hand, if the suspect was to his side he would have to be one hell of a shooter to hit him on the run. He could do it, but then he was one of the best marksmen on the force. One thing he knew was that if he took any more time trying to figure it all out, the suspect would be long gone. Just then, inside the building to his left, he heard a crash followed by cursing. Realizing that the suspect had tripped and fallen, Delany made his move. Hurling himself inside, he rolled to his right, came up with revolver pointed in the direction of the noise, and then began zigzagging his way to the barrels. He was no more than ten feet from safety when he experienced a sharp stabbing pain in his right foot. Instantly, he went into a roll and then quickly crawled the distance to safety. Looking down at his foot he saw a four-inch nail sticking up through his shoe. He wanted to cry out, to release the pain, but held it in for fear of exposing his vulnerability to his adversary. With one hand he held his ankle, with the other he held the gun. His hand was steady. He might be injured, but in no way was he helpless.

"Go on," a slow and deep voice called out from the other side.

"What?" Delany responded, attempting to project confidence in his voice.

"Let it out," came the answer. "Scream if ya want. I saw what happened."

"I don't know what you're talking about," Delany managed.

"Yeah. Sure ya don't," the shooter mocked. "And that there spike in your foot, you don't know nothin' 'bout that neither, right?"

So he knew, thought Delany wincing as the pain began to intensify. He didn't know whether he should attempt to pull the nail out or leave it alone for fear of passing out or bleeding to death. He decided to leave it in.

"I know you over there tryin' to figure out what to do," called the man. "Why don't we just call it a draw and both walk away from here alive?"

"No can do," replied Delany without hesitation.

"That a fact?"

"Yep, that's a fact."

"You one crazy cop, man," snorted the suspect. "One crazy cop."

"Nope," replied Delany rolling over for a better position. "You shot a police officer. Can't let you walk away from that."

"Surely you're not referrin' to old Seth back there?" he laughed.

"You find shooting a police officer funny?"

"No, I surely do not," he mocked. "But old Seth ain't no real police officer."

"Fifth precinct—narcotics. Detective Seth Stevens," countered Delany.

"Yeah, sure, sure. He got a badge and the gun, but he's just another crook out to shake the brothers down for cash."

"You saying he was shaking you down?"

"Tryin'," answered the man. "But it wasn't his turf."

"What do you mean, his turf?"

"Meanin' I already paid the man off to let me work the street. I wasn't gonna pay no more. That's a fact and your good old buddy Seth found that out."

"I'm suppose to take your word for that?"

"Given as how we're in the bind we're in, I guess so."

"Still doesn't change the facts. You shot a police officer."

"Self-defense," countered the suspect. "Old Seth said he was gonna blow my head off. He would have if I hadn't been too fast for him. I got hold of the gun as it cleared his holster. He got so scared he started pullin' the trigger right away and ended up shootin' himself."

"And you just happened to end up with the gun?"

"Right again," answered the suspect. "I sure as hell wasn't gonna return it to old Seth so he could blow my head off."

"Great," muttered Delany softly. "Caught between a dirty cop and a pusher. Just great!" He thought for a second, then said, "Even if what you say is true, you're dealing dope."

"True," admitted the suspect. "I push some dope on the street to make ends meet."

"Stop," taunted Delany, "you're breaking my heart."

"It is how it is."

"What's your name?" asked Delany.

"Reggie."

"Reggie what?"

"Just Reggie."

"Well Reggie, ever hear of a thing called a job?" asked Delany as he quickly checked his foot. The pain was still there, but the intensity had subsided. Maybe he was just getting used to it.

"Oh, yeah. Done that, but the minimum wage thing didn't cover the rent. Got evicted twice. Ended up in public housing and on welfare. Ever been on welfare, man?"

"No."

"Didn't think so. Take it from me it's a real trip—worse than being in prison. I been to prison once. Short time," he added. "And I been on welfare. Ask me, I'd say prison is better. At least you can be a man. On welfare, you nothin' but a whipped dog." The man paused reflectively. "That's how I got this here job. Hooked up with brothers there and they set me up on the street, selling. Since then, I got the whole family out of the projects and pay my bills on time. Best of all, I don't have to go beggin' to the man for a handout."

"And the kids that get hooked on dope?"

"Now you're breaking my heart," he ridiculed. "If you and yours are so concerned for the kids, where were you when I was growing up? I don't recall seein' anyone comin' around tryin' to improve our lives. Truth is, you and your kind could give a rat's ass about us folks as long as we keep our mouths shut and stay off your streets. So don't be handin' me that bullshit 'bout kids and how you're out there protectin' society. Maybe you're too stupid to know it, but your real job is to protect all the corrupt politicians, bankers, lawyers, and judges from people like me who won't play by their rules."

Silence fell between the two men. Delany loosened the strings on his shoe to accommodate the swelling. Delany spoke first, trying to keep the dialogue going. "You know what, Reggie? I can't figure out why you're still here. I thought you'd be long gone out the back."

"The door's welded shut."

"Too bad," muttered Delany. "I guess that leaves us back here."

"Not for long," came the answer from the other side. "I'm aimin' to make my move out the door. Only a matter of time before your friends arrive and then I'm shit outta luck."

"You move—I fire. Trust me on this, Reggie," cautioned Delany. "I'm good, very good."

"Gotta do what ya gotta do," he replied resignedly. "But one thing is true. I'm not doin' no time for shootin' a crooked cop."

"It doesn't have to go down this way," responded Delany quickly. "You say you shot in self-defense. That could make a difference."

Reggie laughed out loud. "And you're gonna get Johnny Cochran to be my lawyer, right?" He laughed again. "Man, you got to be the dumbest cop in the world or you are seriously tryin' to jerk my chain."

"No, I'm serious."

"Well, I'm serious, too. I stand a better chance winnin' the lotto than sellin' the truth to a judge and jury if it came down to my word against a cop's. That's sayin' I even made it to a trial. Seth and his pals have a serious stake in keepin' me quiet. Dead quiet!"

"If that's true, than he'll be coming after you."

"Maybe, maybe not. Could be he'll call it a draw to avoid the trouble. Either way I see it, I'm better off on the streets."

Delany searched his mind attempting to find some middle ground.

"Time's up, Mr. Police Officer," called Reggie. "This is the way it's goin' down. I'm makin' my way to the door. I'll drop the gun once I'm out. You don't shoot and I don't shoot, okay?"

"Don't do it, Reggie," he pleaded knowing that the only way to apprehend the man was to drop him. He pointed his revolver toward the open space leading to the door. He would get one shot and only one shot. Pulling the hammer back on his revolver, he steadied his hand against the concrete floor and waited.

Suddenly, the figure of a man leaped into his line of fire. He was tall and slender—young. No time left...

The Collar   Name_____

Instructions: read each statement before coming to class. Indicate your response by circling "agree" or "disagree" at the end of the statement. In class, discuss the statement with your group and attempt to reach consensus. If consensus is impossible record your vote and write *your* individual response to the statement in three or more complete sentences.

1. If the government provided decent jobs with fair wages, our drug problem would not be as great as it is. Agree or Disagree. **Group Vote: Agree_____ Disagree _____**

2. People like Reggie can never get a fair trial in this country. Agree or Disagree. **Group Vote: Agree_____ Disagree _____**

3. Reggie is right, Delany's real job is to protect corrupt politicians, bankers and judges. Agree or Disagree. **Group Vote: Agree_____ Disagree _____**

4. People like Reggie need to take responsibility for their own actions and quit blaming others for their problems. Agree or Disagree. **Group Vote: Agree_____ Disagree _____**

5. Given the nature of capitalism, there will always be poor people. However, this does not mean the system is bad. Agree or Disagree. **Group Vote: Agree_____ Disagree _____**

6. Generally, people who have wealth have worked hard and deserved what they have. Agree or Disagree. **Group Vote: Agree_____ Disagree_____**

7. The truth is that the drug war is really a war against the poor and racial minorities. Agree or Disagree. **Group Vote: Agree_____ Disagree_____**

8. Even if Officer Steth Stevens was corrupt, it doesn't alter the fact that Reggie was breaking the law selling drugs. Therefore, it's Delany's duty to bring him down. Agree or Disagree. **Group Vote: Agree_____ Disagree_____**

9. The only way to truly win the drug war is to legalize all drugs. Agree or Disagree. **Group Vote: Agree_____ Disagree _____**

10. Martin Luther King believed that those treated unfairly by unjust laws have a right and an obligation to oppose them through civil disobedience. Reggie believes the present laws treat poor people unfairly. Therefore, his actions are justified. Agree or Disagree. **Group Vote: Agree_____ Disagree_____**

Question #1: If you were Officer Delany, would you shoot Reggie or allow him to get away. Why? Be sure to use information and theory from your textbook to support your decision.

Question # 2: If America did decide to legalize drugs, what plan or strategy would you recommend to accomplish the task? Be sure to indicate whether you would legalize only some drugs or all drugs, how you would distribute them, and who would pay the cost of producing them.

Wayward Son

The hysterical sobs were so loud that the door to the bedroom vibrated. Outside, Joe pounded on the door demanding entry. "Shelia," he ordered, "open this door and I mean right now!"

A small, wide-eyed child tugged at his open shirt-tail. "What's the matter with mom, Dad?"

"Nothing's wrong, Danny," he replied too quickly and in a tone he realized was too harsh. Bending down he took the boy's small arms into his hands and attempted to reassure him. "Your mother is a little upset right now. Everything is going to be all right."

"What's she upset about?"

"Damned if I...," he started, but caught himself. "I mean, I'm not sure. But you know your mother—the cat coughs up a hairball and she starts to cry."

"Is it about Pauley, Daddy?" Danny asked.

"Of course not," he replied. "Your brother's away at the university. He's coming home today for Thanksgiving so, he couldn't have anything to do with this."

"But he called this morning," replied the boy meekly as if surrendering a secret.

"And that's when all this began?" Joe asked.

The boy nodded as tears pooled in the bottom of his wide eyes.

Joe turned back to the door and yelled over the sobs, "Shelia, is this about the call from Pauley? If so, I wanna hear about it right now. Open the door this very minute. He's my son, too." Suddenly, the sobbing ceased. From inside, he heard the faint patter of footsteps moving in the direction of the door. The man leaned closer. From the other side he heard inaudible whisperings.

"For Christ's sake, Shelia," he blurted, "you know I can't hear so well. Open the damn door or speak up."

"Give me…," she stopped as she choked out a sob. "Give me a minute. Just let me dry my eyes and then I'll be right out."

"Damn it, Shelia," he cursed. "You know how this makes me crazy when you leave me hanging. Open the door so we can talk."

"In a minute."

Joe was about to reply when he heard Pauley's old Chevy pull up in the driveway. Fitted with straight pipes the car drove him crazy, especially late at night when he was trying to sleep. But right now those pipes sounded as sweet as church music because it meant that he'd finally be able to get to the bottom of this mess. Turning, he headed downstairs. By the time he reached the bottom step, Pauley was walking through the front door.

"Dad," greeted his son with obvious surprise. "What are you doing home, Dad? I thought you'd be working."

"What? I don't have a right to come to my own home for lunch?" he asked in a perturbed tone.

"Yeah, sure," Pauley said quickly. "It's just that you always eat out for lunch."

"Mostly, but today I wanted to have lunch at home. Do I need an excuse?"

"Where's mom?"

"Upstairs making like Niagara Falls."

"Oh, man," muttered Pauley with his head hung low.

"So, it is something with you, huh?" confronted his father. "What's up with you that you're making your mother cry?"

"I'll go up and talk with her."

Joe was going to object, but before he could Pauley was around him and bounding to the top of the stairs.

"Damnit!" he yelled after his son. "I have a right to know!"

"Daddy," whispered his other son who was standing in back of him.

"Yes, Danny?" he asked, turning around having forgotten that his younger son was still there.

"Mommy says you shouldn't swear so much."

"I know. I know, Danny. It's just sometimes people drive you crazy."

"Mommy also says that we shouldn't make excuses for the things we do wrong."

"That's true, too," he defended, "but your mother should also have told you that there's an exception to every rule."

"Does that mean when Tommy Cruthers makes me crazy I can swear?"

"No, you can't," replied his father with controlled patience.

"Why?"

"Because it's not right to swear when Tommy makes you crazy."

"I don't understand."

"I know, Danny," he said, fending off the small child. "It's because of your age. You're too young to understand, but you will when you get bigger, okay?" Before the boy could reply, his father turned to the top of the stairs and shouted, "I have an appointment, but when I get back this evening I better have some answers." With that he pushed his large arms through his overcoat and stomped out of the door leaving the small child to watch him leave.

It was after six that evening when Joe returned home from work. Pulling off his coat he quickly made his way to the kitchen where he heard the voices of his family. It was time to get to the bottom of whatever the hell was going on with this family. Entering the kitchen he was instantly aware of a mood shift. The light laughter and joviality was quickly replaced by an impending sense of foreboding and doom. Pauley was setting the table and Sheila was stirring a large pot of soup and sprinkling spices while looking at him through eyes still puffy from her afternoon crying bout. Danny was working on his homework, but stopped as soon as he entered the room.

"For Christsakes," he exclaimed. "From the looks of you people, you'd think the Gestapo had just entered the synagogue!"

His wife stopped stirring and moved to his side. "Don't be silly and don't swear in front of the boys." Pushing him to his spot at the table, she rushed to the refrigerator. "How about a nice cold beer before we eat, huh?"

"Yeah, sure," he capitulated. "That's a good start. But don't think you're not going to have to explain what the hell all the commotion was about this afternoon." He dropped his 6 foot 3 inch frame into a kitchen chair and then, closing his eyes, he put the bottle to his lips and sucked out a mouthful of beer. Pausing, he let the cold liquid slowly trickle down his throat so as to capture its full flavor. Setting the bottle on the table, he smacked his lips and rolled his thick tongue around in his mouth as if to mop up any remaining liquid lingering in the deep crevasses of his cheeks. Looking up he said, "Times up. Father Joe is here and it's confession time."

"Joe!" exclaimed his wife. "Don't say things like that—it's sacrilegious."

"What's that?" inquired Danny curiously.

"Not now, Danny," said his father wearily.

"Is that something else I have to wait until I grow-up to know?"

"Something like that," his father replied. "Now, someone tell me what's going on." He sat waiting at the table rhythmically rolling fingers across the tabletop. The huge hand took on the appearance of five thick sausages attached to a meaty palm.

Pauley sighed heavily before beginning. "Look Dad, this is going be hard for me, but it's time you knew the truth. I quit the football squad this week."

"You quit football?" choked Joe. "This is your third season. What about all the hard work? What about all the trophies and awards you've won? What about your scholarship?"

"I know, I know," he sighed. "But it's not working for me, Dad. And, as far as the money, I've already got a job in a computer shop to cover tuition. I'll be able to finish my education with the money that I make there."

"So that's it?"

"Well, not exactly."

"What?"

"I'm moving out of the dorm when I return to school after the Thanksgiving break."

Joe slammed his hand down hard on the table, shaking the entire room. "I knew it! I knew it! I knew it the minute you walked into the house this afternoon! You've knocked-up some tramp and you're moving in with her. You're gonna wreck your entire life!"

"Joe!" screeched his wife, crossing herself. "Danny's in the room."

"Relax, Shelia," he said attempting to calm her. "He doesn't understand."

"I do, too," countered the small child quickly.

"No, you don't."

"I do," the boy protested smugly. "It's when you do the big nasty with a girl."

Joe's eyes darted to his wife. She had begun crossing herself again.

"You've been hanging around that Cruther's boy too much. I forbid you to play with him anymore," he ordered sternly.

"It wasn't Tommy," protested Danny. "It was the girls in class. They were talking about it."

"Mother of God," gasped Sheila, racing over to her youngest and wrapping her arms protectively around him as she gently lifted him from his seat. "Danny, you go to your room and finish your homework there. The adults need to talk."

"Do I hafta?" pleaded the boy. "Why do I always hafta leave when it starts getting good? How am I ever going to grow-up if I hafta go to my room all the time?" Resigned to his fate, the small child slid off his chair and trudged slowly to his room, muttering as he went, "Man, I'm gonna be the stupidest grownup in the whole world."

All eyes were on Danny as he disappeared into the dinning room. They waited until they heard his footsteps on the stairs before resuming. "No Dad, nobody's pregnant," began Pauley running his fingers through his hair. "Man, this is so hard. Why does it have to be so hard?"

"Oh, my God," his father interrupted wide-eyed as he jumped from his chair. "You're dying. You've got some strange disease or cancer and you're dying."

"No, I'm not sick, Dad. At least I don't think I'm sick." He turned to his mother who nodded, coaxing him on. Pauley walked over to his father and placed his hand on his shoulder. "Sit down, Dad."

When the man had done so, his son took a chair opposite him. Looking him squarely in the eyes, he began. "Dad, I know you think of me as your football hero. The son who can go onto the field and go up against anyone and prove his manhood. But that's not the truth."

"That is the truth," Joe protested. "I've been to every one of your games. You knocked the big guys on their ass every time. There's the trophies in the living room on the mantel, the pictures of you in the newspapers. Our phone was ringing off the hook with all the big university scouts calling. Remember? What do you mean it's not true?"

"Well, yes," he admitted, "that part of the story is true. But, it's not the whole story."

"What? You were taking those weird steroids to do all that stuff? If so," he said angrily, "I'm gonna kill that bastard high school coach of yours! I always knew he wasn't on the up an' up. It's those damn Germans, they'll do anything to win."

"Dad, please!" begged Pauley. "Just let me talk without all the interruptions. This is hard enough the way it is."

Joe nodded, promising not to utter a single word.

"Dad," Pauley began again in a voice strained with emotion. "You have to know this. I have to tell you."

"What?" he asked, not able to help himself. "You can tell me Pauley. You're my son."

"Okay," nodded the boy pausing again.

With a hand gesture, Joe urged his son to give voice to his thoughts. He waited as Pauley's sigh broke the silence.

"I'm gay," he announced softly.

A deafening silence fell upon the room. Father and son locked eyes. It was Joe who finally broke contact. Leaping up from his chair he roared, spittle jettisoning from his mouth, "What? Is this some kind of joke?"

"It's no joke, Dad. I'm gay."

"Like a queer—a fag?"

"Dad, please don't say that."

"Why? Isn't that what you're saying? That you're a queer?"

"The term is gay, not queer," protested Pauley.

"No! I won't believe this," he protested, waving his arms in the air as if fighting off invisible demons. "No son of mine was born to bend over so some queer guy could..."

"Joe!" shouted his wife. "I won't have that talk in my house."

"Well, you better get used to it, Shelia, because your boy here is telling you that he's a queer and that's what queers do."

"Dad, please listen," pleaded Pauley. "It's not like that."

"Oh, it isn't?" he mocked. "Then why don't you educate you're ol' man, huh?"

Taking in a deep breath Pauley exhaled. "I know how you think about it. That's why it's been so hard for me to admit it to myself."

"What about all the dates with the girls in high school?" his father interrupted.

"Sure, I dated. Everybody dated. I didn't want to be left out. In part, I think it was denial. I thought that if I went out with girls I'd get to the point that I would begin feeling something for them. But, I didn't. No matter how hard I tried it didn't work. The only crush I ever had on anybody in high school was Buddy Henson."

"Oh, Lord," cried Joe, covering his face with his hands. "Shelia, this is all your fault."

"My fault?" she protested.

"Yeah," he spat. "You and your family's wishy-washy liberal ideas. Remember when he was five and wanted the doll for Christmas? I said no, but oh no, you and your wimpy family with their stupid educated ideas went right out and got it for him. They wouldn't listen to an uneducated dago like me. I said it wasn't right—now look!"

"Dad!" exclaimed the boy. "It has nothing to do with dolls or anything else. I was born this way. It's genetics."

"That's crap!" Joe countered. "It has nothing to do with genes. Look at me. I ain't ever had a perverted thought in my life. And your mother there, she was given the *Ladies of the Holy Alter* award last year. She's practically a saint! The monsignor said so himself when he presented the award. I'll tell you about genetics. You were born Italian. Italian men are great lovers. Ask anyone, they'll tell you. Women love Italian men and Italian men love women. The whole world knows that."

Pauley shook his head. "No, Dad. It's not that way and I'm tired of living a lie. I've made up my mind, I'm coming out of the closet."

"The closet?"

"I want to live my life openly."

"Oh, my God!" Joe said, thinking about the implications. "The monsignor, what's the monsignor gonna say? You're Catholic. This is a sin. He'll excommunicate you! You'll go to hell for sure."

Sheila rushed over to her husband. "No, Joe, don't think that way. God's not gonna send Pauley to hell. How could He condemn Pauley when He Himself made Pauley this way? It don't make sense."

Joe buried his hands in is face and then muttered, "No, you're wrong, Shelia. The Bible says it's a sin. Truth is truth. If God had changed his mind he would have had someone write a sequel. I'll tell you what the problem is today. Everybody wants to blame their problems on somebody else. Now it's God. What ever happened to free will and taking responsibility for your actions?" He stopped, and then turned to his son.

"Look, Pauley, we'll get you help. We'll get you straightened out. Nobody has to know."

"No!" Pauley responded emphatically. "It doesn't work that way. I'm gay and I'll always be gay. And I am sick and tired of hiding in the closet. I'm coming out. I'm going to live my life. I'm entitled to a life!"

Joe was going to respond when he suddenly stopped. His face withered to a mass of pain. "Oh, God," he finally whispered looking toward the stairs. "Danny, what about Danny? If you come out of this closet you're in, he's going find out. It's gonna kill him. He'll be tortured by the other kids."

"No, Dad," interjected his son. "That's one of the reasons I'm home. I want to talk to Danny. I love him. I want him to hear it from me. I want to explain it to him. I don't want him to hear about it from some bigoted kid with warped parents who have no idea what they're talking about. He's older than you realize. He can understand. Trust me, Dad."

Joe opened his mouth to speak but stopped when the bell to the front door rang. "Who in the hell could that be?" he asked, looking out the bay window onto the front porch. Outside stood a young man.

"That's Jerry," announced Pauley.

"Who's Jerry?"

"Jerry's my friend—my special friend."

Joe hung his head. "You don't mean...like boyfriend?"

"More like lover," replied Pauley with his mother at his side. "We've been lovers for six months. I love him and he loves me, we're a couple, Dad."

"What's he doing here on my doorstep?"

"I asked him to come and stay the weekend, Dad. I wanted you to meet him. Tomorrow, Jerry and I are participating in a protest march on city hall. We want the same rights you and mom have."

"Oh, my Lord," Joe muttered painfully, looking outside again. It had begun to snow now. Large, heavy flakes carried on a bitter, brisk wind descended to the ground as if vainly attempting to cover earth's imperfections. He glanced back at the young man braced against the cold on his front porch. Clutched in his arm was a package neatly wrapped and bowed. So, he thought, the suitor comes bearing gifts. Suddenly, the epic story of the Trojan horse leaped into his mind. Beguiled and foolish, the Greeks had opened their gates and allowed the enemy's entry into the very heart of their sanctuary. Was this, he wondered, his Trojan horse?

Wayward Son   Name_____

Instructions: read each statement before coming to class. Indicate your response by circling "agree" or "disagree" at the end of the statement. In class, discuss the statement with your group and attempt to reach consensus. If consensus is impossible record your vote and write *your* individual response to the statement in three or more complete sentences.

1. Pauley's only chance at finding happiness is to accept who he is and openly live a gay lifestyle. Agree or Disagree. **Group Vote: Agree_____ Disagree _____**

2. Homosexuality is morally wrong because it violates the laws of nature. Agree or Disagree. **Group Vote: Agree_____ Disagree _____**

3. Generally speaking, when a child drifts toward homosexuality, the parents are to blame. Agree or Disagree. **Group Vote: Agree_____ Disagree _____**

4. Joe's real problem is that he is homophobic. Agree or Disagree. **Group Vote: Agree_____ Disagree _____**

5. If Pauley reveals his homosexuality, Danny is bound to suffer irreparable psychological damage. Agree or Disagree. **Group Vote: Agree_____ Disagree _____**

6. The real problem in this case is the outdated idea that homosexuality is a preference rather than an orientation. Agree or Disagree. Why? **Group Vote: Agree____ Disagree____**

7. Accepting homosexuality as normal would greatly undermine the stability of society. Agree or Disagree. **Group Vote: Agree____ Disagree____**

8. Homosexuals should enjoy the same rights as heterosexuals including marriage and the right to adopt children. Agree or Disagree. **Group Vote: Agree____ Disagree____**

9. In general, men are more homophobic than women. Agree or Disagree. **Group Vote: Agree____ Disagree ____**

10. Since religious teachings clearly condemn homosexuality as sinful, it would be wrong to give our blessing to its practice. Agree or Disagree. **Group Vote: Agree____ Disagree____**

Question #1: If you were Joe would accept your son's decision to openly live a gay lifestyle? Why? Be sure to use information and theory from your textbook to support your decision.

Question # 2: In your view, should homosexual couples be afforded the same rights as married heterosexuals? Why? Be sure to use information and theory from your textbook to support your decision.

ISBN: 1-886202-08-7